REGENERATIVE RETROFIT:
California's First Living Building

An Ecotone Publishing Book/2020
Copyright © 2020 Juliet Grable

Ecotone Publishing — an Imprint of the International Living Future Institute

For more information write:

Ecotone Publishing
1501 East Madison Street Suite 150
Seattle, WA 98122

Author: Juliet Grable
Book Design: Johanna Björk, softfirm
Edited by: Fred McLennan

Library of Congress Control Number: 2020932567
Library of Congress Cataloging-in Publication Data

ISBN 978-0-9972368-9-7

1. ARCHITECTURE   2. ENVIRONMENT   3. PHILOSOPHY

First Edition

Printed in Canada on FSC-certified paper, processed Chlorine-Free, using vegetable-based inks.

REGENERATIVE RETROFIT:

California's First Living Building

LIVING
BUILDING
CHALLENGE

CONTENTS

nex·us

/ˈneksəs/

noun

1. a connection or series of connections linking two or more things.

2. the central and most important point or place.

Architectural Nexus has created a building that is a NEXUS— a nexus of people, ideas, industries, and visions—a centrally important place. It is a visionary building linking past, present, and future in a capital city situated on the confluence of two rivers. Although known for innovation and leadership, California is plagued with drought, wildfires, and lack of affordability.

On April 17, 2018 the Arch Nexus SAC office became the 19th Living Building Challenge project in the world, and the first in California. Let me say that again. The first in California! Given the size of California's economy, given the pace of physical growth through construction, and given the reputation and the major impact this State has as an environmental leader, to earn the first Living Building is a significant achievement and testament to this team's dedication to the environment, to the community of Sacramento, and to future generations. Personally, I love that this is happening in Sacramento – not Los Angeles, not San Francisco, not Berkeley, but Sacramento – the heart of California, the heart of the fifth largest economy in the world, and my hometown from age 11 to 18 years.

Arch Nexus is also the first architecture firm to have its own Living Building. Many firms are committed to sustainability and helping their clients—pushing their clients—to create sustainable buildings; however, Arch Nexus is walking their talk and living their values. They are not only challenging their clients to do what is right with their buildings, they are doing it

themselves, and with that bold action they are demonstrating true leadership and showing the way for others to follow.

With the creation of this building, Arch Nexus concretely manifests its responsibility and commitment to help address the pressing social and environmental issues we collectively face, including climate change. This Living Building stands for HOPE in our future. It shows that our actions can have positive effects, that we can live in harmony with nature and with each other, and that we can be vital, beneficial, contributing members of the ecosystem, both natural and human, in which we live.

The Living Building Challenge consists of twenty Imperatives covering seven Petals or performance areas. This building met all twenty of the ambitious and rigorous Imperatives within the following seven Petals: Place, Water, Energy, Health + Happiness, Materials, Equity, and Beauty.

By achieving the Place Petal through the adaptive reuse of an existing building (the first Living Adaptive Reuse), this project demonstrates Arch Nexus' commitment to celebrating the history and culture of this unique place, to honoring natural areas, and to deepening our connection to the food we eat and the ecosystems in which we live.

By achieving the Water Petal in a state often suffering from severe drought, this project demonstrates that we can drastically reduce water use and live within the carrying capacity and the natural flows and cycles of our watersheds. Arch Nexus has worked hard with local regulators to chart the way for other projects to follow.

By achieving the Energy Petal, this project is demonstrating climate-related leadership and resource resiliency. It shows that we can significantly reduce our energy use and generate more power than we need from renewable sources. At the time of this book's printing, the building has far surpassed its targets by generating 176 percent of its energy needs.

By achieving the Health + Happiness Petal, this project provides an optimal work environment for occupant health, well-being, and productivity, with a deep connection to place.

By achieving the Materials Petal, this project is eliminating hundreds of the worst-in-class chemicals from the building materials and protects the health of the people inside the building, the people in the factories who made the materials, the people in the communities near those factories, and the people who installed the materials. It also protects the health of the watershed by eliminating those chemicals from run-off, pollution and waste streams that can contaminate the air, soil, and water.

By achieving the Equity Petal, this project benefits the local community, promotes person-to-person interaction, and assures that everyone has access to and benefits from this project. This project also helped to create jobs in the region, support the local economy and protect old growth and native forests.

By achieving the Beauty Petal, this project has not only created a beautiful building that delights everyone who visits, it has also created a building that inspires and educates others.

Anyone who has visited Living Buildings knows that there is something about them that is deeply impactful; they speak to both your mind and your heart. When folks first hear about the Living Building Challenge they may ask, "How is that possible?" But after visiting and experiencing a Living Building like this one they say, "Why isn't every building like this?"

That question represents a moment of transformation with profound ripple effects – impacting how people think about the world and what they expect from their buildings. This project has indeed had a profound impact on the larger community. When it started, there were not any projects in the region pursuing the Living Building Challenge and now there are numerous initiatives at a variety of scales, including single family homes, education buildings, large

multi-story office buildings, and whole neighborhoods. Arch Nexus SAC is touching hearts, changing minds, and inspiring actions. It is literally changing the landscape of the region and those changes are for the betterment of the environment, communities, and families now and for generations to come.

The culture of Arch Nexus is evident in this building and in their on-going work in Sacramento, Salt Lake City, and nationally. They are leaders in the green building movement and leaders in showing how for-profit businesses can operate from a place of generosity and abundance, bringing about authentic and meaningful change. Inspired by the experience of creating this building, the firm is working on more Living Building Challenge projects, donating time and expertise to Living Affordable Housing projects, sharing tools, knowledge, and lessons learned openly with other architects and the industry and community at large, as well as hosting countless tours, presentations, and conversations to help others to move toward a Living Future.

This building is a physical manifestation of what is possible: how humans can cultivate restorative ecosystems in which buildings can benefit both human and natural communities. I encourage you to explore this book for the story of this building, the people who made it, and the positive influence it has generated. I hope it acts as a catalyst for change, inspiring you to think, ask questions, and have conversations about where you live, work, learn, and play and how your community can support a Living Future that is ecologically restorative, socially just, and culturally rich. Enjoy!

KATHLEEN SMITH

3

ACKNOWLEDGEMENTS

I am honored to have been given the opportunity to tell the story of Arch Nexus SAC. As we face the ever more urgent threat of climate change and the challenge of growing inequities, we need projects and stories like these to rejuvenate our spirits and strengthen our resolve. This project, so much bigger than the sum of its parts, could not have happened without the contributions of many, and I have been truly humbled by the passion, dedication, and positive energy surrounding its creation.

So too, this book could not have happened without the contributions of many. Whether core members of the design and construction team, Arch Nexus staff, or representatives from the City of Sacramento and SMUD, many people generously shared their time with me so that the documented story of Arch Nexus SAC might accurately reflect the richness and depth of the actual experience. Special thanks to Kenner Kingston, Brian Cassil, Patty Karapinar, Erica McBride, Jennifer Styduhar, Jeff Davis, Robb Harrop, Sean Kotke, Kenny Dees, Wendy Nelson, Jay Reiser, Charlie Downs, Mark Buehrer, Kathleen Ave, and Jennifer Gress. **As this list cannot represent everyone who participated in this ground-breaking project, I would also like to acknowledge everyone else who contributed time, knowledge, and enthusiasm to Arch Nexus SAC.**

I would like to especially thank Kenner Kingston and Brian Cassil of Arch Nexus—Brian for working closely with me on all aspects of the draft, for facilitating introductions, coordinating meetings, and sourcing photos and graphics; Kenner for his insightful feedback and articulate explanations. Both gentlemen were truly a pleasure to work with, and it was my honor to witness not only their passion for the Living Building Challenge,

but their clear dedication to shepherding an architectural design firm into a Stage 5 company—a humane and inspiring organization that makes a lasting and positive impact. Thanks to you, Life is great!

I would also like to acknowledge Patty Karapinar and Erica McBride for answering my many questions and for always being available for a quick call. Finally, many thanks to Josh Allred for the many artful photographs that grace these pages and bring the story of Arch Nexus SAC to life.

I would like to thank Michael Berrisford of Ecotone Publishing, whose firm but gentle hand guided this project to successful completion, Fred McLennan for his editorial excellence, and Erin Gehle and Johanna Björk of softfirm, whose deep understanding of architecture and artistic design so complements and captures the spirit of Arch Nexus SAC.

Thank you, Jason F. McLennan, Amanda Sturgeon, and everyone else at the International Living Future Institute, for providing an uncompromising vision of where we need to go.

The work of Arch Nexus, or that of any Living Building design team, cannot occur in a vacuum. I would like to acknowledge the many agencies, organizations, and individuals who are working toward creating more sustainable, resilient, equitable, and livable communities, including the City of Sacramento, SMUD, the Sacramento City Unified School District, Community Rebuilds, and the BLOCK Project.

Finally, I would like to thank my husband, Brint Borgilt, for his continued support.

AUTHOR PROFILE

JULIET GRABLE

Juliet Grable is a freelance writer and editor whose work covers a range of topics related to sustainability. Juliet is the author of two other Living Building Challenge case study books: *Brock Environmental Center for a Living Chesapeake* and *Desert Rain House*; she also served as editor on *Creating Biophilic Buildings*, another Ecotone publication. Juliet has served as Managing Editor for *Green Builder* Magazine and has contributed to many national and regional publications, including *Earth Island Journal, Sierra, Audubon,* and *Home Power.* In addition to stories about regenerative design and construction, her writing covers innovative water systems, wildlife conservation, and watershed restoration. Juliet is grateful to live in Oregon's Southern Cascades with her husband Brint, cats Pico and Binx, and pup Roca.

PART I

Responding to Drought

The First Living Building in California

7

REGENERATIVE RETROFIT: *California's First Living Building*

Naturally weathering metal panels and an artistic bicycle rack welcome anyone first entering the Arch Nexus Sacramento office.

THE FIRST LIVING BUILDING IN CALIFORNIA

The first thing you notice when you walk through the front door of Arch Nexus SAC is a curving wall of green which stretches from the welcome desk in the lobby and into the open office. Once inside, the building feels immediately comfortable. You hear the low murmur of voices. A dog pads up to greet you. The workstations are illuminated with warm filtered light.

From outside, through the glass, one can see people at work in a small conference room, leaning toward each other and talking with animated gestures. On the corner sidewalk, a pedestrian lingers near a bench, then decides to sit under the canopy of a generous cork oak tree. Further down the street, employees from neighborhood businesses are strolling to an outdoor café for lunch.

This 9,000-square foot building, located at the corner of R and 10th street in the city of Sacramento, represents the 19th fully certified Living Building project in the world, the first Living Certified project in California, and the first that is an adaptive re-use of an existing building. It is home to design professionals who practice for Architectural Nexus, a people-driven firm with projects across the West. Arch Nexus designed the project and owns and occupies the building.

To understand the project's significance, you must first understand the context in which it came to be.

9

Part I: **RESPONDING TO DROUGHT**

LAND OF EXTREMES

No other state is as receptive to myth-making as California. It is a land of extremes, subject to epic flooding, years-long droughts, and landscape-shaping earthquakes, wildfires and landslides.

The Golden State also boasts the fifth-largest economy in the world and produces a bounty of fruits, nuts, dairy, and vegetables that are exported across the country and beyond. For decades, people have been lured West by California's many natural treasures: the beaches and rocky headlands that make up her coast, the deserts' spare beauty, the majesty of the Sierra, and the extreme scale of the Redwoods and Sequoias, not to mention the centers of human creative capital, which include the Meccas of Hollywood and Silicon Valley.

California also faces epic challenges, many of which are being heightened by climate change. Cities along the 840-mile coastline are bracing for sea level rise. Predictions call for more extreme weather events, more severe flooding, prolonged droughts, extended wildfire seasons, and wildfires of greater intensity. Annual snowpack, which supplies at least one third of the state's water, is predicted to decrease by 48 to 65 percent by 2100. The state is already wrestling with who will lay claim to a finite supply of water, and how to leave enough to ensure healthy fish runs. One of the most intense droughts in California history ended in 2017, and the last few years have seen record-breaking wildfires, some of which ripped through suburban communities, leaving hundreds of people homeless and compromising air quality for tens of thousands for weeks on end.

California has earned a reputation for progressive policies, and the state is responding to the threat of climate change with aggressive carbon reduction goals.

In 2006, then Governor Arnold Schwarzenegger signed a law which required California to reduce carbon emissions to 1990 levels by 2020. The state reached this goal four years early, and in 2016 Governor Jerry Brown upped the ante with SB 32, which requires the state to reduce carbon emissions by 40 percent by 2030.

To achieve these targets, California has instituted a cap-and-trade program, required utilities to embrace renewable energy, and incentivized electric vehicle adoption. California also boasts the most progressive state-wide building energy code in the country. Title 24, part of the California Building Standards Code, sets step-wise targets on the way to achieving zero net energy (ZNE) use in all new homes by 2020 and in commercial buildings by 2030. Increasingly, the state is also turning to water recycling and reuse, although there are still considerable hurdles to implementing solutions on the building scale.

The Sacramento skyline with the iconic Tower Bridge spanning the Sacramento River.

THE MOST LIVABLE CITY

Sacramento, the state's capital city, began as a Gold Rush town that sprang up at the confluence of the Sacramento and American rivers. Even though it was the seat of government, until recently Sacramento suffered from something of an inferiority complex, facing inevitable comparisons with the more dramatic cities like San Francisco.

Today the city has come into its own as a diverse and cosmopolitan urban center with distinctive hipster and foodie cultures. Located in the heart of the Sacramento Valley, in the northern part of California's great Central Valley, its economy draws from a healthy mix of agriculture, tech, healthcare, and

world-class universities. In 2018 the city's population topped half a million, and it is the fastest-growing big city in the state.

Sacramento has also earned a reputation as an eco-friendly city, thanks to progressive leadership and a public utility committed to a diverse renewable energy portfolio.

The building of the railroad turned Sacramento into a bustling center of commerce.

However, Sacramento faces many of the problems as other modern American cities, including sprawl, traffic congestion, and an inadequate supply of affordable housing. It is also in the crosshairs of climate change.

With an annual rainfall of less than twenty inches and six months which average less than one inch of rain, Sacramento is vulnerable to droughts. It has also been identified as one of the nation's cities most at risk for catastrophic flooding.

Snowpack from the Sierra feeds the Sacramento River, which carries over 30 percent of the state's runoff. As temperatures warm, more precipitation will fall as rain. Instead of being captured in winter snowpack, it will flow downslope, overwhelming streams and rivers.

The city of Sacramento has spent millions on flood control in recent years, primarily on detention basins and upgraded pumping stations. There is also a plan to raise nearby Folsom dam and to widen two major bypasses, which divert water into floodplains during heavy rain events.

"Sacramento wants to be a place where people want to live. The city's goal is for people to come here and want to stay and raise their families here. Our planning has gone back to how do we make it great for people? If we're just building stuff and it doesn't respond to people, then there's really no purpose in what we're doing. If we don't create great places, then we're failing the community as a whole."

BRUCE MONIGHAN
City of Sacramento

"Goals are not enough. You really need action. That's really what we are trying to change here in Sacramento."

JENNIFER GRESS
California Air Resources Board

"There's a causeway as you're headed out towards Davis from Sacramento, and from there you can see that it goes from farmland to a lake almost as far as the eye can see during the spring. That's where all the overflow of water goes to avoid the city from being flooded."

JEFF DAVIS
Arch Nexus

But the city has also embraced its role in reducing its contributions to climate change. In 2010, the city drafted its first Climate Action Plan, or CAP, for internal operations. The community-wide Climate Action Plan, released in 2012, detailed goals for reducing emissions from transportation and buildings, reducing waste, expanding the urban forest, and preserving farmland.

In March 2015, the community-wide CAP was adapted into the city's 2035 General Plan. It outlines specific strategies, including mixed-use development that encourages walking and biking, use of public transit, solar energy deployment, and architectural design that reduces heat gain. It also promotes green building practices such as recycled construction materials and water conservation. Many of these strategies were chosen not only to help reduce the city's carbon impact, but to help achieve the complementary goal of making Sacramento the most livable city in the country. Unfortunately, at the time of printing, the ambitious goals set forth in the CAP have remained largely aspirational, as many of the key strategies were scaled back, or lacked the resources for implementation.

It was in this context, as the most intense drought in decades reached a crisis point, that a local architecture firm called Architectural Nexus first approached the city with a plan to transform an old warehouse into a Living Building that generated all of its own energy and used captured rainwater for all of its water needs.

THE CENTRAL VALLEY

One of the most productive agricultural regions in the world, California's Central Valley produces tomatoes, grapes, cotton, apricots, and 60 percent of the world's almonds.

Framed by the Sierra Nevada Mountains to the east and the Coast Range to the west, the valley receives snowmelt into two massive river systems: the Sacramento to the north, and the San Joaquin to the south. Together these rivers drain one-third of the entire state.

The Central Valley is blessed with rich soils laid down by regular flooding. The hydrology created a tapestry of productive landscapes: salmon-bearing streams, riparian zones and wetlands, and vast grasslands. At one time these ecosystems supported millions of migrating birds and large herds of grazing animals, including pronghorn antelope, tule elk, and mule deer.

But over the last one hundred fifty years, human activity has severely altered this landscape. Massive dams, levees, and other diversions capture water for hydro-electric power, farming, drinking water, and flood control. More than 90 percent of wetlands have been drained for agriculture, and only 1 percent of the original native grassland is still intact.

If the 20th century was about shaping the land for our supposed benefit, the 21st century may well be remembered as the era of restoration. In the Central Valley, projects to restore habitat, improve water quality, and restore natural flows have begun, as well as efforts to preserve open space and restore native grasslands. As we fully embrace this task, Living Building Challenge projects will set the tone, showing how human development can work with nature, rather than taking from her, to the benefit of all.

13

THE FIRST REGENERATION

Architectural Nexus is a medium-sized architectural firm with two offices: one in Salt Lake City, Utah; the other in Sacramento, California. The firm specializes in large institutional clients, and its projects include civic buildings, healthcare projects, research laboratories, work for the federal government, and mixed-use and resort properties.

Architectural Nexus formed in 2003, with the merger of two medium-sized Salt Lake City firms, Jensen Haslem Architects and Thomas Petersen Hammond Architects.

Just a few years later, the country began sliding into the economic downturn that was to become the Great Recession. It was a scary time. In 2008, the Arch Nexus partners in Salt Lake City office realized that the best thing they could do for their business was to move from leasing space to owning it. It was a buyer's market, and they found an existing building for a reasonable price.

The building, a 1950s-era concrete block structure, had served several long-term tenants over the years, including a fitness center. At the time it had been vacant for several years. But

the building had good bones, and the partners, including a young principal named Kenner Kingston, saw the potential to transform it into a comfortable, modern and sustainably-designed office that also attracted like-minded clients. Their goal was to achieve LEED Gold or better.

As part of the retrofit, a new 4,000-square-foot main entry lobby was designed to connect the existing portions of the building. Builder Jacobsen Construction also performed seismic upgrades and added a new conference room. Later, an upper floor was added in a follow-up phase to the original project.

Completed in 2010, the project earned LEED v3 BD+C Platinum in 2011. With an emphasis on energy efficiency, regionally manufactured and recycled materials, and creating pleasant,

14

"We decided then that we would be our own building manager for the learning opportunity. We wouldn't outsource it; we would just do this work ourselves. And for the next two years, we proceeded to work through all the problems. We went from a really high EUI down to the target EUI and even below the target EUI, driving and measuring and increasing comfort. That changed my point of view on performance standards and how important they are."

KENNER KINGSTON
Arch Nexus

inspiring spaces both indoors and outside, the project anticipated many of the Imperatives of the Living Building Challenge and laid the groundwork for Arch Nexus Sacramento. Today, the 30,000-square foot building serves as the main offices for the firm's Salt Lake City design professionals.

Here are some of the project's highlights:

ENERGY: Efficiency measures ensure the building uses half the energy of a typical office building of similar size. The building envelope was enhanced with extra insulation, high-performance windows, and a new roof. Exterior window shading prevents glare and unwanted solar heat gain but facilitates daylighting. The mechanical system was upgraded to high-efficiency rooftop units, and an on-site solar PV array generates 13 percent of the building's energy usage.

SITE: Asphalt was converted to landscaped terraces which host native and adapted plants. These areas help reduce stormwater runoff and mitigate the heat island effect. Shaded outdoor spaces encourage people to gather. A smart irrigation system responds to weather forecasts and minimizes water use.

DAYLIGHTING: To optimize daylighting for staff, Arch Nexus conducted daylight analysis for the first (but certainly not the last) time. On the remodeled ground floor, a central daylight courtyard brings in sunlight to the open office. Tubular skylights create a daylit office space in a second-floor addition called The Loft.

MATERIALS: Strong preference was given to regionally manufactured, rapidly renewable, and recycled materials. For example, wood flooring from the building's fitness center was repurposed as decorative elements in the ceilings and walls.

The building environment positively influences occupants and visitors. But the work did not stop with construction. The building was not located in an area convenient to public transportation, so Arch Nexus instituted an alternative transportation program to encourage carpooling, biking, and the use of the company's electric vehicles. The firm soon learned that by occupying a building they had designed, they had created a learning opportunity.

15

LEARNING
BY DOING

Architectural Nexus had set a high bar with its Salt Lake City headquarters. But the partners were about to learn an important lesson. The project was complete: the building looked good, but it was not performing as they had hoped.

"Like a lot of LEED buildings, it was uncomfortable," says Kingston. "But we couldn't figure out why." The partners had not received warranty training, and the O&M manuals were not ready on time. Finally, it was discovered that the building controller had reversed AM and PM on the building schedule, and it was wreaking havoc on energy efficiency and comfort.

For Kingston, it was an "aha" moment.

"We decided that operations were important, and that the thing architects do where they just hand the building off to owners and say 'good luck' wasn't good enough."

Arch Nexus took over the management of their own building and began to educate themselves on the role of occupant behavior. Slowly but surely, the building began performing to its potential, and in 2014, the project earned LEED v3 O+M Platinum—one of only a few buildings across the country to achieve a Platinum rating in two LEED rating systems.

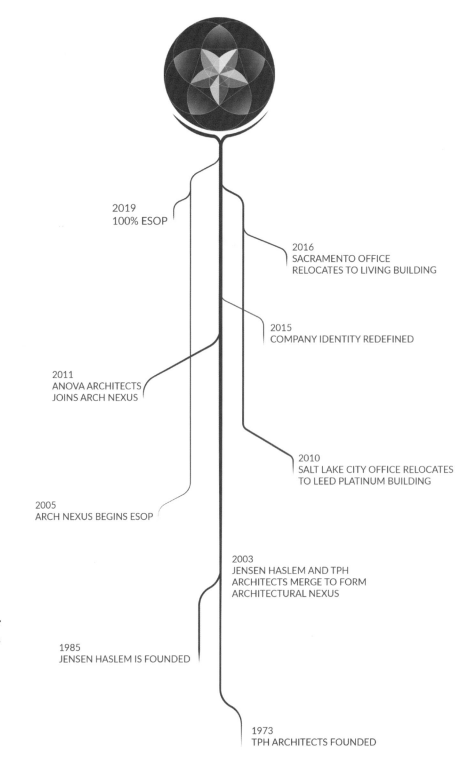

2019
100% ESOP

2016
SACRAMENTO OFFICE
RELOCATES TO LIVING BUILDING

2015
COMPANY IDENTITY REDEFINED

2011
ANOVA ARCHITECTS
JOINS ARCH NEXUS

2010
SALT LAKE CITY OFFICE RELOCATES
TO LEED PLATINUM BUILDING

2005
ARCH NEXUS BEGINS ESOP

2003
JENSEN HASLEM AND TPH
ARCHITECTS MERGE TO FORM
ARCHITECTURAL NEXUS

1985
JENSEN HASLEM IS FOUNDED

1973
TPH ARCHITECTS FOUNDED

16

INSPIRATION STEWARDSHIP REGENERATION

From June of 2014 until today, we've been in a constant process of redefining ourselves and kind of perfecting who we are. There's been a massive focus on culture.

That's when I first started saying, I think the millennials are right; I think they figured it out. We're in a purpose economy and they're going to be our bosses someday before we retire.

If you give an architect a problem, they will naturally try to solve it with architecture. But we have realized that buildings are not actually the point. The point of architecture is human experience, not the building itself. It's just a stage for human experience to occur. People are what matters, not buildings. Not that the craft of architecture isn't important—it is, but only to the extent that it creates a meaningful experience for people.

KENNER KINGSTON
Arch Nexus

BUILDINGS ARE NOT THE POINT

In 2011, hoping to better weather the economic downturn, Architectural Nexus merged with California-based Anova Architects. Anova itself consisted of two firms with deep roots in Sacramento and the Sierra Foothills: Murray and Downs, headed at the time by Charlie Downs, and Oshima and Yee, a small firm started by Alan Oshima in the 1960s and later joined by Joe Yee. When the two firms merged, in 2007, Anova became the second largest firm in the region, with offices in both Sacramento and Placerville, California.

After Arch Nexus merged with Anova, the enlarged organization peaked at over one hundred fifty design professionals, with headquarters in both Salt Lake City and Sacramento, putting the firm in a good position to serve the entire Western United States and competitively bid for projects once the Recession eased.

Soon after the merger with Anova Architects was complete, in early 2014, principal Kenner Kingston became president of the company. At this point, Arch Nexus was a diverse partnership of twenty-plus principals practicing in a variety of markets.

Still, the partners hadn't really come together around a common purpose other than the business itself. As one of his first projects as president, Kingston wanted the partners to establish a more unified identity.

"The younger partners especially started to say, what can we do? How can we help? And that started to create a culture transformation," says Kingston.

Over the course of several retreats, the partners rebranded their firm, launched a new graphic identity and website, and developed an understanding of their common goals. As part of this process,

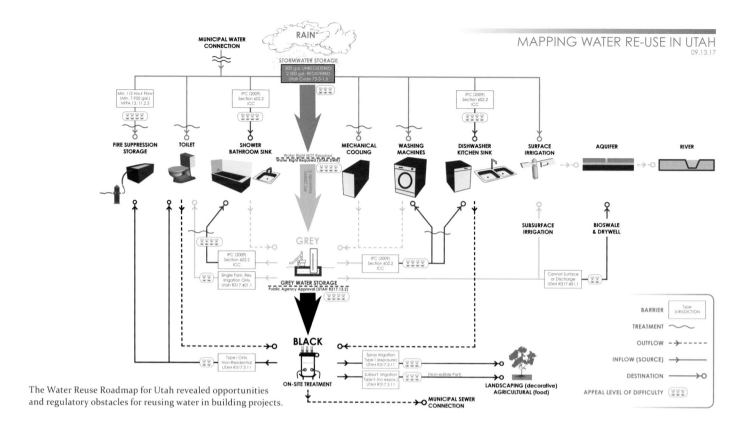

The Water Reuse Roadmap for Utah revealed opportunities and regulatory obstacles for reusing water in building projects.

they identified three core values that aptly defined their business's purpose: Inspiration, Stewardship, and Regeneration.

Buildings were no longer the point; they were a means to an end. Instead of a group of twenty design partners with twenty separate practices who just happened to share a building and rent, Arch Nexus was evolving into a purpose-led organization with a shared identity and goals.

But the firm wanted to go further. Their intense self-analysis led to some interesting discoveries. For guidance, they looked to David Logan, who identifies five stages of "tribal leadership" that may be experienced by organizations. According to Logan, every organization consists of tribes: groups of people who share a common culture. By understanding its own culture and level of functioning, an organization can deliberately set about improving it—and consequently, its employee satisfaction and success.

For example, members of Stage 1 tribes—the lowest level—are "despairingly hostile." They may even steal from the company or threaten violence. Stage 3 companies are healthier, but members compete with each other and prize individual performance above all else.

Arch Nexus had achieved Stage 4. At this stage, members believe "We're great"; they unite around a core set of values and are generally happy and healthy. But Stage 4 groups are also very competitive, and they see other firms as rivals. In contrast, Stage 5 companies believe that "Life is great." At this stage, the enemy dissolves; instead of competing against other people or other firms, members compete against a phenomenon or concept, such as homelessness or climate change. Stage 5 organizations are at the leading edge of innovation, and often create new market opportunities which allow them to embark on game-changing projects. Arch Nexus, Kingston claims, is in the process of deliberately transforming from a Stage 4 to a Stage 5 company— the kind of organization that changes the world, and that takes on the Living Building Challenge.

SETTING THE STAGE FOR A LIVING BUILDING

Although Arch Nexus SLC was an exemplary project and one of the first LEED Platinum projects in the region, they had failed to address a critical dimension of sustainability.

During a client a tour of the building, someone asked Kingston about water reuse. Although Arch Nexus SLC had an efficient irrigation system and low-flow fixtures, they hadn't considered water reuse at all.

"I had no good answer beyond a lack of understanding of the regulations around water reuse in Utah in general and Salt Lake City specifically," says Kingston.

Shortly after this exchange, Kingston reencountered the Living Building Challenge at the 2011 Greenbuild conference. He attended a session on the water systems proposed for the Oregon Sustainability Center and was introduced to the Oregon Water Reuse Roadmap for the first time. This roadmap illustrates the different potential paths for water reuse and the regulatory obstacles, if present, for each of these paths.

A spark was lit.

Kingston gathered a small group of like-minded individuals to create a water reuse roadmap for Utah. This illuminating process revealed that Utah had many more regulatory barriers to water reuse than did Oregon. Kingston did not give up on the idea of implementing water reuse in a project, but he decided to wait for the correct opportunity. Meanwhile, in 2012, he became an Ambassador for the ILFI.

Shortly after the acquisition of Anova was finalized, in 2014, the Sacramento staff found themselves in a similar position to the Salt Lake City office before the regeneration of Arch Nexus SLC: tenants in a building designed by another architecture firm, at the mercy of fluctuating rents. The leadership at Arch Nexus wanted the Sacramento staff to enjoy a rich, healthy work environment that was on par with the Salt Lake City office.

"We knew the kind of value we built for the firm by buying and regenerating and owning and operating our own building," says Kingston. "We knew we could have the same thing in Sacramento if the economy would let us do it."

Owning and operating their own building would enable the firm to build shared value and stabilize costs, and they could create a physical manifestation of their core values.

Around this time, several factors converged to make a Living Building in Sacramento a real possibility.

The drought in California had reached a crisis point. The period between 2011 and 2014 had been the driest on record. Snowpack was nonexistent, and Governor Brown warned of rationing and new regulations. If ever the time was ripe for a project that confronted the reality of drought and offered solutions for mitigating it, this was it. At the same time, the economy was beginning to bounce back.

The partnership realized that this was the time to act. Once the drought ended, the opportunity to do something radical would likely end, too. In May of 2015, the Arch Nexus partners initiated a real estate analysis.

THE NEXT REGENERATION

The Arch Nexus partners understood that regenerating a building can help reduce the building sector's energy consumption and avoid developing new sites. Choosing a previously developed site for their Salt Lake City office, for example, had preserved two acres of open space or other undeveloped real estate, and reusing rather than tearing the existing building down had saved tens of thousands of pounds of materials from the landfill. Repurposing existing buildings also precludes the need for new municipal infrastructure and utility system extensions.

The partners asked their real estate agent to show them pricing trends for Sacramento's mid-town zone. They quickly limited their choices to properties close to light-rail stops, in the sweet spot inside the transportation loop but just outside of downtown.

By June, they had narrowed the options from ten to a single-story building on the corner of R Street and 10th. It wasn't the most affordable option, but none were as "livable" as this one. The building, which had served as a warehouse, was located in a safe and highly walkable neighborhood close to downtown and light rail. The R Street corridor, an up-and-coming neighborhood studded with historic brick buildings and a bustling dining and entertainment scene, was also attracting artists and design firms.

Although dated, with drab vertical siding and a heavy mansard roof, the building had good bones. A line of mature London planetrees shaded the building on one side. Railroad tracks shone through the pavement, hinting at the street's history as an industrial corridor.

Later in June, Arch Nexus initiated the purchase. The next month, they invited a select group of firms to submit proposals.

It was time to get to work.

"We want to take existing building stock and find an adaptive reuse for it. That's the start of the most sustainable thing you can do: to not tear it down and build something new, but rather take something that's there and adapt it to how you want it."

BRUCE MONIGHAN
City of Sacramento

"R Street was an up-and-coming and vibrant place. Our timing was perfect."

CHARLIE DOWNS
Arch Nexus

The regeneration of Arch Nexus SAC transformed a humble warehouse (top) into a Living Building (bottom) while staying close to the original footprint and retaining most of the original structure.

21

PART II

An Authentic Vision

Making Biophilic Connections

23

Part II: **AN AUTHENTIC VISION**

REGENERATIVE RETROFIT: *California's First Living Building*

One of the goals of the Arch Nexus SAC project was to create a healthy and inspiring workspace that sends a message of transparency.

SETTING THE VISION

Arch Nexus now owned a building in Sacramento but was also still paying rent for office space for their Sacramento staff; in addition, the fact that Arch Nexus is an employee-owned company raised the stakes.

If the project went over budget or took longer than expected, it would have a direct impact on stock prices, which are valued annually and based on the fair market value of the company's assets. Consequently, the partners wanted to complete their Living Building project as quickly as possible. Their ultimate goal was to complete construction and move into the building by the end of 2016; otherwise, the company's stock prices would be impacted for the following year.

To finance the project, the partners turned to Zions Bank, a bank headquartered in Salt Lake City with which Arch Nexus enjoyed a long relationship. When the bid cost of the project exceed the appraised value of the property—which was largely based on the lack of comparable buildings in the area—Arch Nexus CFO Jeff Thorpe worked with Zions bank to secure bridge financing to make up the difference.

"These Living Buildings are unicorns. Their value is really difficult, if not impossible to appraise. Their value goes beyond what can be measured."

BRIAN CASSIL
Arch Nexus

A DIVISION OF LABOR

From their experience in Salt Lake City, the Arch Nexus partners understood the importance of keeping the roles of the owners and architects distinct.

With that in mind, Kenner Kingston and Charlie Downs agreed to take on the role of the owner's representative. Joe Yee was the Principal-in-Charge, and principal and architect Jeff Davis ran the project on a day-to-day basis. Davis brought a background in sustainability and public interest design to the table. He played a key role in developing initial design concepts based on place and biophilia, and later worked with the City of Sacramento and state officials on permitting issues, particularly the water systems. Director of Design Robb Harrop, who oversees all of the firm's design projects, worked with Davis to turn the biophilic inspirations into a working design, focusing particularly on the aesthetics of the building. Principal Holli Adams oversaw the day-to-day production and consultant coordination.

Patty Karapinar, Director of Sustainability and an associate architect with Arch Nexus, took on the daunting task of vetting materials for the Red List. She worked closely with the builders throughout design and construction, and as construction commenced she took on the role of Construction Administrator. Several other Arch Nexus staff collaborated on the interior and landscape design.

ENGINEERS AND EXPERTS

With its team of talented architects, landscape architects, and interior designers, collaboration was already part of the Arch Nexus company culture; however, the partners understood that a Living Building Project would require working closely with the builders, engineers, and other key team members in an integrated design process.

Kingston collaborated with Yee to select the team. Taking a systematic approach, they created a spreadsheet that listed all extant Living Buildings and their team members. They were not just looking for firms and individuals with expertise and good reputations; they wanted ones that shared the Arch Nexus ethic—companies that were trying to "walk the walk" rather than being led by their clients.

DPR, a national commercial contractor and construction management firm with a deep portfolio of sustainable projects, was brought on to provide pre-construction design services.

Arch Nexus invited Mark Buehrer to join the team to help design the water systems. Buehrer is founder and director of 2020 ENGINEERING, an engineering consulting firm based in Bellingham, Washington. He had lent his expertise on several Living Building projects, including the Bullitt Center and the Bertschi School, and was a passionate advocate for water systems that emulate natural systems. He brought to the table extensive experience implementing Low Impact Development (LID)

strategies for a variety of building typologies, including schools, commercial buildings, and municipal projects.

Glumac, a large engineering firm that was pursuing Living Building Challenge certification for their Shanghai headquarters, was hired as the engineer of record.

Arch Nexus brought on Jay Reiser of Miyamoto International, a global earthquake, structural engineering and project management company based in California, to provide structural engineering and seismic upgrades. Warren Consulting Engineers, a firm with decades of experience in site development throughout Northern California, served as civil engineer. Hunt Electric, a Salt Lake City-based firm with which Arch Nexus had worked several times, acted as the project's solar energy consultant.

As the project progressed, Arch Nexus hired Capital Engineering as the commissioning agent. The firm had deep roots in the Central Valley, a long relationship with the Sacramento partners, and extensive portfolios in civic, healthcare, and educational projects.

"We're part of this community. We come to community meetings; we are involved in our street partnership. So we wanted to support Arch Nexus in what they were endeavoring to do regardless of whether we got the job."

WENDY NELSON
MarketOne

SELECTING A CONTRACTOR

Kingston knew that transforming the building on R Street into a Living Building would cost more than a conventional project, and more than even a LEED Platinum project. But the estimate they had received from DPR exceeded the company's budget. Faced with proceeding without pursuing the Living Building Challenge, Kingston decided on a risky move: they would solicit hard bids from several firms, including DPR.

One of these was a local construction company called MarketOne. A firm with about seventy employees, MarketOne specializes in adaptive reuse and commercial interiors, as well as industrial, healthcare, and biotechnology projects and data centers. Although they take on projects in all of the Western states, their home base was in Sacramento.

MarketOne had recently finished up an adaptive reuse project of their own on R Street, just a few blocks down from the building Arch Nexus was purchasing. The 24,000-square-foot project entailed a complete renovation of the interior, including new windows, insulation, and a new roof, and it had earned LEED Gold certification. This regenerated brick warehouse building now serves as offices for MarketOne and an architecture firm.

Around this same time, Arch Nexus held the first of several public meetings during which they sought community input about their project. Curious about their new neighbor, Wendy Nelson of MarketOne attended these early meetings. As they learned more about the proposed project, they realized Arch Nexus shared a passion for sustainable design and community-mindedness.

Nelson invited Downs, Kingston, Yee, and Davis to tour their regenerated building. The Arch Nexus partners liked what they saw.

Not only was MarketOne's bid the most competitive, the firm promised to be an ideal partner with whom to share what was sure to be a journey full of ups and downs. At the time, no one at MarketOne knew much about the Living Building Challenge, but they were excited to take it on.

28

AN ALLY AT THE CITY

In another bit of serendipity, architect Bruce Monighan had recently taken a position as Urban Design Manager at the City of Sacramento. A variety of design project proposals landed on Monighan's desk. When he learned about Arch Nexus' plans to regenerate the building on R Street, he immediately recognized the project's significance—not so much as an economic driver, but as a real manifestation of the direction city leaders claimed they wanted to go.

Monighan was familiar with the Living Building Challenge; now he had to get everyone else on board.

"There was an early outreach effort to help educate a few key people about what was coming down the line," says Monighan. "The fact was, the requests we were going to be getting [from Arch Nexus] were going to be dramatically different than standard practices." He realized the key was going to be to maintain flexibility, and he persuaded others to be receptive to unconventional approaches.

Sacramento Municipal Utility District, or SMUD, was also a valued partner early on, and Ray Nalangan and Michelle Friedrich of SMUD attended the initial design charrette. The utility was originally engaged to help Arch Nexus qualify for incentives through Savings by Design, a statewide program which encourages high-performance design and construction. But the partnership developed into much more. When Kathleen Ave, Senior Climate Program Manager in Energy Strategy for SMUD, learned about the Arch Nexus project and the Living Building Challenge, she recognized it as a means for transmitting good intentions into action. SMUD was to become a partner, not just for this individual building project, but for collaborating on shared goals and disseminating the principles of the Living Building Challenge throughout the region.

"When this project came forward as a Living Building Challenge project I thought, whoa, this is really serious. There is like nothing like this happening around here. And nobody in the city knows anything about this. This is going to blow up all of the boundaries of all of the rules."

"I'm not sure this can happen easily in every city. The key is partnership with the people who have the ability to say yes or no. And I think that we had a distinctly good partnership."

"Lots of people talk about net zero and the 2030 Challenge and all of that, but they don't do it. This was it. This was happening. And so there was really no alternative but to allow this project to happen."

BRUCE MONIGHAN
City of Sacramento

"I've been through many iterations of some of these plans at the city and observed the challenges to getting to action despite good words on a page. So when I learned about Living Future and this project I got really excited, realizing that it solves so many of the problems that I had observed, not just from my role at SMUD, but as chair of the Capitol Region Climate Readiness collaborative."

KATHLEEN AVE
SMUD

29

One of the creators of Luna Cycles, artist Jay Stargaard (seated right) chats with a friend and one of the mayor's advisers during the open house celebrating the completion of Arch Nexus SAC.

ENGAGING THE COMMUNITY

As the resident expert on public engagement, Davis saw an opportunity to integrate the goals of the Living Building Challenge with public interest design, even though Arch Nexus was not a public entity.

After all, reasoned Davis, all buildings exist in the public realm, even privately-owned buildings. With this in mind, he approached Kingston and suggested that they let their project be guided by the principles developed by SEED.

Short for Social Economic Environmental Design, SEED's stated mission is "to advance the right of every person to live in a socially, economically, and environmentally healthy community." The organization offers a methodology for a participatory design process that activates a range of voices.

The first step was to engage the community. Arch Nexus held a series of three public meetings, the first of which took place on August 10 of 2015. They invited a variety of stakeholders from the surrounding neighborhood, including local business owners, residents, and a couple of people who were experiencing homelessness at the time.

Arch Nexus gave a short presentation explaining who they were and why they wanted to move into the building on R Street, but they did not share design concepts. The purpose of the first meeting was not to inform the community what they were planning to do, but to ask community members how Arch Nexus, as a new neighbor, could contribute to the community.

In the discussion that followed, community members described their concerns and desires. They were especially interested in how Arch Nexus could participate in the neighborhood's lively arts scene. They also described what they saw as the specific social, economic, and environmental issues affecting their neighborhood—increased traffic, for example. Much of the feedback was addressed and incorporated into the biophilic design process.

For example, some people had suggested that they wanted a place where they could stop and rest as they walked up and down the street while shopping. Davis added a bench in front of the Design Lab in direct response to this public input.

Similarly, some of the artists who had studios nearby asked if Arch Nexus would be willing to participate in Second Saturday art walks. In response, the design team conceived the conference room and lobby as informal gallery space that could showcase local art.

"I think more than anything, what people wanted to hear was that we wanted to be part of a community that was already strong," says Kingston.

During the second meeting, on October 10, many of the same stakeholders showed up, curious about how the design was proceeding. A third meeting followed, during which Arch Nexus revealed the final design and showed how the community feedback had been incorporated.

SEED PRINCIPLES

- Advocate with those who have a limited voice in public life

- Build structures for inclusion that engage stakeholders and allow communities to make decisions

- Promote social equality through discourse that reflects a range of values and social identities

- Generate ideas that grow from place and build local capacity

- Design to help conserve resources and minimize waste

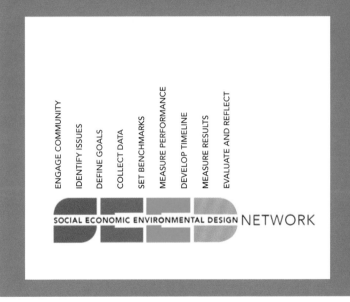

WORKING WITHIN CONSTRAINTS

32

By its nature, an adaptive reuse of an existing building comes with more design constraints than a new construction.

In this case, the team was limited by several factors. They had to more or less stay within the original footprint and work with the existing structure and one-story floorplan. The brick building immediately adjacent would have implications for shading. A row of London planetrees on the building's east side, while valuable for shade and beauty, would impact daylighting and solar PV generation. The roof would have to serve multiple functions, supporting solar modules and HVAC equipment but also skylights that brought natural light to all parts of the building interior. The space available for urban agriculture was severely limited. An unsightly guy wire ran from a utility line to the ground, slicing diagonally through the air over the existing asphalt parking area on the north side of the building.

Nonetheless, the partners were excited for the opportunity to transform this humble building into an inspiring workplace that might spark or contribute to the regeneration of an entire neighborhood.

A BUILDING PROJECT BASED ON BIOPHILIC PRINCIPLES

Arch Nexus initiated the purchase of the R Street property in June of 2015. The design team was selected by mid-June. Shortly after that, in early July, the team's key members flew to Seattle to visit two Living Buildings: the Bertschi School and the Bullitt Center.

This "precedent trip" not only gave the team confidence that they could accomplish their goals, it gave them a chance to bond and develop a sense of shared purpose.

Just as the Arch Nexus partners understood that an integrated design process was key to the project's success, they also made the early decision to not only incorporate biophilic design principles, but to let these principles lead the design.

Back in Sacramento on July 10, they hosted a charrette focused on biophilia in the building on R Street. The entire team attended, along with representatives from SMUD. It was there under fluorescent lights and acoustic ceiling tiles that the team was first asked to think deeply, not about solar calculations or ventilation strategies, but about place.

Kingston, Downs, Yee, and Davis had conducted some preliminary research about the human and natural history of the site, and they presented their findings to the rest of the team.

They had learned as much as they could about the Delta ecosystem before it was impacted by Europeans, about the indigenous people who thrived there, and about the district's more recent past as a railroad corridor. They contemplated the site's relationship to the confluence of the Sacramento and American Rivers, and the special ecosystem of the alluvial plain, born out of regular flooding. They learned how the city has responded to flooding over the decades, and pondered the implications of climate change for the City's future.

During the all-day intensive, participants were asked how regenerating a building in Sacramento could address several environmental imperatives, including climate change, pollution and toxins, habitat destruction, potable water security, resource destruction, and the human-nature connection. For example, how could this project address the realities of flooding and drought while contributing to the restoration of the native ecosystem? Post-It notes quickly filled the board.

One of the first tasks was to identify constraints, such as the shade cast by the row of London planetrees, as represented by the green circles.

"I love the story Arch Nexus told about paying homage to the railroad and to R street and the history, kind of walking the whole team through that during the charrette. Every time I walk over those railroad tracks, I remember that story. I think that was a really cool way to start and to actually pay homage to this area and the history here. It's more than just the building; it's a piece of the fabric of the community."

JAY REISER
Miyamoto International

"What architects are asked to do in terms of understanding place is really site based; it's site analysis. What we tried to do here was really to get into the history of place, the nature of place. And this exploration informed the biophilic strategy for the building."

KENNER KINGSTON
Arch Nexus

The team was introduced to the Petals of the Living Building Challenge and the elements and attributes of biophilic design defined by Stephen Kellert. They were asked to think about each Petal in the context of biophilia.

Again, the ideas flowed. The team identified several biophilic strategies for their project, including indoor and outdoor gathering spaces, indoor and outdoor gardens, weathering, operable windows, abundant daylight, quality views, cultural connections and references, and robust community outreach.

The first charrette was followed up by a second design charrette on July 13, during which the biophilic ideas were organized into a direction for design. On July 17th, the project was formally registered with the International Living Future Institute under Living Building Challenge 3.0.

PAYING HOMAGE TO PLACE

During the biophilia charrette, the team honed in on the place-based relationships they wanted the building design to reflect. First described by Stephen Kellert, these relationships describe connections between buildings and the distinctive geographical, ecological, and cultural characteristics of particular localities. These connections can be expressed in any number of ways, through building orientation, material selection, and even the highlighting of certain views.

GEOGRAPHIC CONNECTION TO PLACE:
The burgeoning city of Sacramento responded to the reality of flooding by elevating the railroad tracks by several feet; later, the rest of the city was brought up to the same level. The building on R Street, located just a short distance from the confluence of the Sacramento and American Rivers, was built atop seven feet of fill. The building aligns with Sacramento's city grid, which angles approximately 18.5 degrees off from true north. Davis and his team felt the building design should reflect both its relationship to true north—the "earth's grid"— and its location in an historic floodplain.

HISTORIC CONNECTION TO PLACE:
Before European settlement, indigenous people from the Maidu and Miwok tribes thrived in the Sacramento Valley region, using native plants for food, shelter, and clothing. More recently, a railroad ran through the R Street corridor, which served as an industrial warehouse district; remnants of the tracks still shine through the street. The team was struck by the interplay of lines and rhythms evoked by these histories— the organic vertical rhythms of native grasses and the patterns seen in indigenous clothing and

headdresses, as well as the more regimented arrangement of the railroad ties and tracks. Hence, "Reeds and Rails" became one of the major design themes.

ECOLOGICAL CONNECTION TO PLACE:
The Sacramento Valley is defined by water. Flooding was a normal occurrence in the spring and helped create a rich alluvial floodplain that was part of a diverse and thriving landscape that included riparian forests, wetlands, prairie, and savannah. The team learned about key plants that thrived in the marshes and floodplain, including a native bunchgrass called *Nassella pulchra* and marsh tule, an important shoreline plant. The team felt strongly that the design should reference these ecological connections.

CULTURAL CONNECTION TO PLACE:
This once-busy industrial warehouse district had been in decline for several decades but was in the process of transforming into a bustling arts and design community. It was important to send a strong signal that Arch Nexus wished to participate in community life and help the neighborhood thrive.

35

A BIOPHILIC BUILDING

The next task was to translate the intense background on history and place identified during the charrettes into a biophilic building, an effort led by Jeff Davis and guided by Robb Harrop. Biophilic principles shaped the decision-making process going forward.

Every design element and every material was held up to the same litmus test: does it enhance or strengthen the biophilic principles? If the answer was no, it was eliminated. The design began to coalesce, with several distinct elements that sprang directly out of the exploration of place and the biophilic principles collectively identified by the team:

- An entry sequence that aligns toward true north and historic R Street, honoring the "earth's grid" and sending a positive and welcoming message of openness to the community.

- A glass-fronted Design Lab that connects to the conference room on the interior and is highly visible from the street in front the building, promoting transparency and curiosity.

- A Living Wall of plants that welcomes people into the heart of the building and serves as a visual symbol of the firm's values.

- An exterior aesthetic and palette that reflects the site's natural and human history and celebrates the geography and ecology of the region, as captured by the "Reeds and Rails" theme.

- Urban agriculture that supports pollinators and harkens back to the biodiversity of the alluvial plain when it was an intact, healthy ecosystem.

- An open office illuminated largely by natural light and arranged into "Neighborhoods" which encourage collaboration and interaction.

- Visible water systems that collect, treat, and manage water, working with the region's natural cycles of rain and drought to supply all of the needs of the building and its occupants.

- The extensive and visible use of local, recycled, and salvaged materials, including a public art installation commissioned from local artists, which celebrates and honors the beauty, history, and true value of our physical resources.

"The indigenous people used nature to create these really strong repetitive rhythms that were important in their culture. So we started to look at rhythms and how that can intersect with place, which grew into one of the strong themes for the building design."

JEFF DAVIS
Arch Nexus

"We had to learn to be very selective. We had to get down to the root. You couldn't put things in the building that weren't meaningful. We questioned everything, whether a material or an aesthetic element or a design move. Does it enhance that biophilic experience? And if an element didn't strengthen those biophilic principles, it didn't make the cut."

ROBB HARROP
Arch Nexus

> *"One of the most common boxes that we have to fit within is budget. If you think outside that box and then bring the design back into it, you're going to have better and more stuff in that box than had you just confined it to the box from the beginning."*

JEFF DAVIS
Arch Nexus

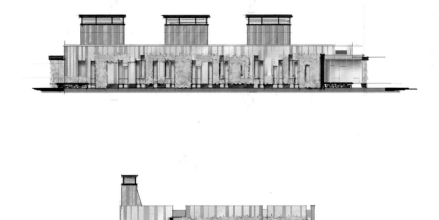

Early Rendering of Solar Chimneys

GREAT DESIGN FOR ANOTHER TIME

Due to the realities of the site and budget constraints, several features were altered or eliminated as the team moved through the design process. In each case, the team was able to find an alternate solution that worked just as well, if not better.

A NEW BASEMENT FOR COMPOSTING UNITS:

The team designed a small basement room to be excavated directly underneath the bathrooms; this way, all waste could feed into the composters via gravity. However, constructing a basement would require shoring up the foundation of the adjacent building and a stair which would take up valuable real estate. The team determined to design a solution that did not rely on gravity, and ultimately selected vacuum-flush toilets that rely on a highly efficient pump and very little water.

GROUND SOURCE HEATING AND COOLING:

A ground source heat pump takes advantage of the near-constant temperature of the earth. A series of wells runs fluid from the building to the ground, where heat is exchanged. The designers considered locating the wells underneath the building, but the drilling rigs were taller than the building. Turning this constraint into an opportunity, they added a row of clerestory windows to the design, which would require a portion of the roof to be removed. They reasoned that the drilling rig could be brought in and the wells dug before the clerestory windows were installed.

However, the cost estimate for the clerestory element proved too much, and they could not justify demolishing a portion of the roof just to accommodate the drilling rig. In the end, the team decided on a highly efficient variable refrigerant flow (VRF) system in lieu of the ground source heat pump.

SOLAR CHIMNEYS FOR NATURAL VENTILATION:

Solar chimneys work on the principle that heat rises. Throughout the day, warm air would rise and exit through the solar chimneys, drawing in air through a row of vents located below the windows and creating a continuous draft that would cool the building. A fluid dynamics study confirmed that the system would provide enough airflow to preclude the need for mechanical systems; however, the cost analysis revealed it to be prohibitively expensive. The revised design included a mechanical system plus operable windows and vented skylights which manage airflow in a similar fashion as the solar chimneys.

37

PART III

The Challenge in Practice

Addressing each Petal of
the Living Building Challenge

An aerial view of Arch Nexus SAC clearly reveals
two major design constraints: shade from a row of
street trees and a limited roof area for solar modules.

Part III: **THE CHALLENGE IN PRACTICE**

The edible landscaping
plants cast pleasing shadows
on the office interior.

REGENERATIVE RETROFIT: *California's First Living Building*

"The human built environment must reconnect with the deep story of place and the unique characteristics found in every community so that story can be honored, protected and enhanced."

LIVING BUILDING CHALLENGE 3.0

The following seven chapters focus on the individual Petals of the Living Building Challenge:

1. PLACE
2. WATER
3. ENERGY
4. HEALTH & HAPPINESS
5. MATERIALS
6. EQUITY
7. BEAUTY

Although the chapters in this section are presented in the order that they appear in Living Building Challenge 3.0, the process of design and construction was not so linear; instead, project teams often contemplated many Imperatives at once, and stories that appear in one chapter could easily fall under another chapter. For more information on the seven Petals and twenty Imperatives of the Living Building Challenge, please visit **living-future.org**.

41

THE PLACE PETAL

Welcoming the Neighborhood

42

43

THE PLACE PETAL
LIVING BUILDING CHALLENGE VERSION 3.0

PETAL INTENT

The intent of the Place Petal is to realign how people understand and relate to the natural environment that sustains us. The human built environment must reconnect with the deep story of place and the unique characteristics found in every community so that story can be honored, protected and enhanced. The Place Petal clearly articulates where it is acceptable for people to build, how to protect and restore a place once it has been developed, and how to encourage the creation of communities that are once again based on the pedestrian rather than the automobile. In turn, these communities need to be supported by a web of local and regional agriculture, since no truly sustainable community can rely on globally sourced food production.

PETAL IMPERATIVES

- Limits To Growth
- Urban Agriculture
- Habitat Exchange
- Human Powered Living

REGENERATIVE RETROFIT: *California's First Living Building*

Arch Nexus SAC is part of a larger trend of redevelopment occurring within Sacramento's core.

The intent of the Place Petal is to realign how people understand and relate to the natural environment that sustains us all. Collectively, the four Imperatives under this Petal seek to cultivate an environment that promotes human interactions and forges connections with the physical environment, culture, history, and ecology of place.

The team's intensive investigations into place and biophilia yielded several themes which would drive the design of the building regeneration and help create those strong connections.

By regenerating an existing site and building, the project avoids developing new land and complies with the first Imperative 01: Limits to Growth. As the first Living Building that is a reuse project, Arch Nexus SAC serves as an inspiration, encouraging other project teams to consider repurposing an existing building rather than building new.

45

The Place Petal: WELCOMING THE NEIGHBORHOOD

A SCALE-JUMPING SOLUTION

The team knew that meeting the requirements of Imperative 02: Urban Agriculture was going to be difficult. The building on R Street is located in Transect L4: General Urban Zone. This transect is comprised of light- to medium-density mixed-use developments.

The Living Building Challenge Standard sets a required percentage of urban agriculture for projects based on their floor area ratio (FAR), which is a measure of the building's footprint compared to the total lot area. With a FAR between 0.5 and 0.74, the percentage of urban agriculture required for the Arch Nexus project was 25 percent, or 3,496 square feet. Unfortunately, very little area was available for landscaping.

Arch Nexus SAC directly adjoins another building to the west and is located just a few feet from the property lines on the north and east. Besides that, the City of Sacramento prohibits edible plantings in the strip between the sidewalk and the street. Parking dominated the south side of the property, and while the team looked at ways to minimize this paved area, they still had to meet the requirements of the Americans with Disabilities Act and allow room for an electric vehicle charging station.

Even though Arch Nexus' landscape architects utilized every bit of available ground and even incorporated vertical trellises into the design, they still could not satisfy the 25 percent requirement; in fact, urban agriculture at the Arch Nexus SAC site comprises just 1,345 of the 3,496 square feet required.

The team decided to take advantage of Scale Jumping, an allowance in the Living Building Challenge which lets a project share resources or infrastructure with a neighboring property when a solution is not possible or practical on the project site alone.

Patty Karapinar had a connection with Rachel Chard, Sustainability Manager for the Sacramento City Unified School District. The district already had a robust program of community gardens in place, which school staff utilized to help connect students with natural cycles and learn about ecological principles such as water conservation and composting. They had even designed a rainwater collection system for one of the gardens.

SUTTER MIDDLE SCHOOL PLANTER PLAN

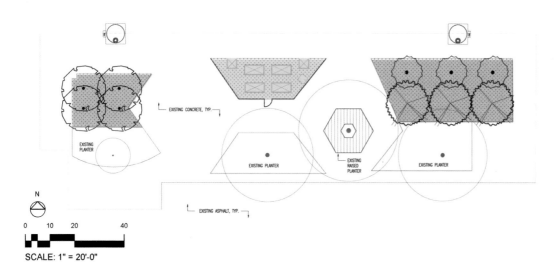

EXISTING CONCRETE, TYP.

EXISTING PLANTER

EXISTING PLANTER

EXISTING RAISED PLANTER

EXISTING PLANTER

EXISTING ASPHALT, TYP.

N

0   10   20   40

SCALE: 1" = 20'-0"

Karapinar contacted Chard to see if the district might be interested in creating an urban agriculture garden at one of their sites. It just so happened that the principal of nearby Sutter Middle School had recently reached out to Chard, wanting to do something with a "dead space" in the quad area. Nicole Costanzo, a science teacher at the school, had been wanting to start a gardening club for her students. Arch Nexus had found the perfect scale-jumping site.

Arch Nexus landscape architect Jennifer Styduhar worked with Chard and Costanzo on the design for the gardens at Sutter Middle School. Located prominently in the quad area between the main building and playground, the gardens are designed according to Living Building Challenge principles. All materials used in the project were vetted to be free of Red List chemicals, and plants are irrigated with rainwater that is collected from the roof of the main school building and gravity fed to two above-ground cisterns. Signage educates passers-by about the gardens and the Living Building Challenge.

Both Arch Nexus and MarketOne donated labor and materials toward creating the gardens. For Arch Nexus, the project was a welcome test of their relatively new philanthropy program, which includes community volunteering and charitable giving components.

The gardens were first planted in time for the 2017 school year. Since their creation, Sutter Middle School students have enjoyed growing a variety of flowers and vegetables, including carrots, beans, greens, and pumpkins, even sharing the bounty with visitors during fall harvest events. Native plants have since been installed. Under Costanzo's guidance, students monitor water levels and irrigation schedules to ensure they won't run out of water during the dry season. They have also begun collecting and saving seeds.

47

ON-SITE URBAN AGRICULTURE

Upon purchasing the property, Arch Nexus recognized that the site's greatest living assets were a row of London planetrees that had likely been planted by the City of Sacramento in the early 20th century, and the large cork oak that graced the corner of R and 10th Streets. The team wanted to preserve and highlight these trees.

The cork oak was incorporated into a new "parklet" on the corner, and the entry elevations were raised to keep the concrete from resting on the roots. Raising the elevations created a high curb, a safety hazard which the design would need to address.

The team wanted to restore as much of the available area as possible to a healthy, diverse ecosystem which provides food and habitat for native pollinators such as butterflies.

Sacramento's climate is characterized by wet winters and summer drought. Plants were selected that could thrive under these conditions and in the site's sunny and shady micro-climates.

Shrubs were planted in the narrow strip between the building and sidewalk. These include fruit-bearing perennials such as evergreen currant, blueberry, and strawberry, along with

medicinal plants like lavender and sweet woodruff. Vines bearing kiwi and passionfruit wind up vertical trellises and have become part of the building exterior's design aesthetic.

Non-edible plants were carefully selected to attract pollinators, protect planting beds, and attract native fauna for pest control; these include California gray rush, Parry's agave, and Thompson's flowering maple.

Employees tend a seasonal garden in a semi-private outdoor space on the building's south side, just adjacent the parking area. There they grow tomatoes and peppers in summer and peas and bok choy during the cooler seasons.

All of these plants are irrigated using collected rainwater.

CREATING PLACES

By orienting the new entry toward R Street and true north, Jeff Davis hoped to send a message of openness to the community. The design team also wanted to enhance the area around the entry into a welcoming space which incorporated the community feedback gathered from the initial SEED charrette.

With that in mind, Davis designed a "parklet" for the corner of R and 10th Streets which centers around the magnificent cork oak and transforms the former asphalt parking area into a destination. Davis worked with the city to resolve several issues, including how to protect pedestrians from the steep curb and diagonal guy wire.

The design was to include a bench where people could rest and a bicycle rack that would encourage pedal-powered transportation. The R Street community had already established a tradition of playful public art installations throughout the neighborhood, and Arch Nexus decided to recruit a local artist to create a design for an artistic sculpture that could double as a bike rack. Charlie Downs managed the effort and sent a Request for Proposals to several local artists.

Jay Stargaard and Deanna Marsh were selected to create the installation. Both of these regional artists already espoused sustainability in their practices, including the incorporation of recycled materials and use of renewable energy to power

49

"Initially the city said they didn't want any plants or benches there. It's a warehouse district; they wanted it clean and open. But as we were meeting with the city to resolve the issue of the curb and guy wire, we asked, what if there's a bike rack and benches there? We didn't even mention plants. They said, what if you put some plants there, too?"

JEFF DAVIS
Arch Nexus

"One of my favorite aspects of this project was working with Jay and Deanna—how fun they were to work with and how visionary they were. And the fact that we were able to support some local artists was also really cool."

PATTY KARAPINAR
Arch Nexus

"The art element is a guardrail, a bike rack, public art, and a place of respite all at the same time."

KENNER KINGSTON
Arch Nexus

"When Deanna and I go for a project, we think about function: If I was biking, what would I need? We knew we wanted some kind of bench, a place where you could put your gear, your backpack, and change your shoes. It's also beautiful, and it adds that wood element."

JAY STARGAARD
Artist

their studios. The artists attended a Living Building Challenge orientation session and worked closely with the Arch Nexus team to ensure their design complemented the project's themes and reflected the firm's mission.

Their sculpture, called Luna Cycles, consists of interlocking hand-hammered steel circles embellished with kiln-formed glass elements representing the phases of the moon. Stargaard and Marsh also added benches made from reclaimed wood to their

sculpture. The benches cantilever off of each end, providing a convenient place for cyclists to rest or change their shoes.

Aside from serving as a place of respite, public art, and a rack that can accommodate up to eight bicycles, the sculpture also doubles as a code-compliant handrail that blocks access to the steep curb and guy wire. Steel planters further enliven the parklet, and the diagonal guy wire, once an eyesore, is now part of an interesting urban composition.

BACK TO THE ROOTS

Early on, the team honed in on several plants that they felt captured the essence of place. Two of these were marsh tule and a native bunchgrass called *Nassella pulchra*.

The marshes that once lined the Delta were dominated by tule. This marsh plant helps buffer against wind and water, provides habitat, reduces erosion, filters nutrients, and helps facilitate the growth of other plants. Tule was an important plant for wildlife and for indigenous people, who used tule reeds to construct canoes and as a building material. They also wove tule into their baskets, mats, and clothing, and boiled or roasted the bulbs for food.

Nassella pulchra, which has the common name of purple needlegrass, is adapted to periodic drought and can store water in its dense root systems. The state grass of California, *Nassella pulchra* was thought to be the dominant grass species across much of the state at one time. It was also an important plant to wildlife and to the area's indigenous residents, who harvested the seeds. However, the team came to question the common assumption that native grasslands were dominated by this single plant. It was much more likely that the native prairie supported a diversity of grasses and forbs, or wildflowers, which in turn supported a variety of pollinators. The team pledged to honor and support biodiversity with the project's urban agriculture.

51

REGENERATIVE RETROFIT: *California's First Living Building*

CONTRIBUTING TO A WALKABLE, BIKEABLE NEIGHBORHOOD

Imperative 04: Human-Powered Living states that each new project "should contribute toward the creation of walkable, pedestrian-oriented communities and must not lower the density of the existing site." The R Street neighborhood context offered great potential for the Arch Nexus project to contribute to this goal.

The up-and-coming arts and design district is close to public transportation and includes a mix of residential and commercial development, with ample shopping and popular restaurants. It is also flat, making it ideal for walking and bicycling, and many streets include well-marked bike lanes. In fact, the site boasts a Walk Score of 90 and a Bike Score of 99, according to walkscore.com.

The Human-Powered Living Imperative includes a number of requirements. The project must supply secure, sheltered bicycle storage, and the design should contribute to the enhancement of pedestrian routes. The project team must also take on an advocacy role to "facilitate the uptake of human-powered transportation."

In addition, projects located in Transects L4 to L6 must provide a transit subsidy for all occupants of the building if the building is owner occupied. (If it is not, tenant employers must provide such a subsidy.) The project must also incorporate showers and changing facilities that can be accessed by all occupants of the building, and at least one electric vehicle charging station.

The parklet and bicycle rack sculpture transformed an unappealing industrial corner into an inviting walkway, sending a clear message of welcome to pedestrians and cyclists alike. The renovated Arch Nexus SAC office includes a dedicated changing room with showers and lockers and both indoor and sheltered outdoor bike storage. Arch Nexus also provides a company bicycle, which was supplied by a former employee who builds custom bicycles. The small parking lot includes an EV charging station equipped with two chargers, which employees are encouraged to use. But Arch Nexus goes a step further by providing a zero-emissions vehicle for company use.

Shortly after initiating the renovation of their Salt Lake City office, in 2010, Arch Nexus purchased two Toyota Prius hybrid gas-electric vehicles to serve as "pool vehicles" that any employee could use. The Salt Lake City office is located in a hilly suburban neighborhood, which makes taking public transportation and bicycling to work more challenging. However, knowing they had access to the company vehicles encouraged some employees to leave their own cars at home.

For the Arch Nexus SAC project, the partners decided to upgrade to an all-electric Chevy Bolt, which has an extended range of over 200 miles on a single charge. The EV has proven so popular in Sacramento that Arch Nexus has traded in the two Priuses at their Salt Lake City office for Bolts and installed two charging

"It's an interesting dilemma that having a shower in the locker room is not really enough to achieve the Human-Powered Living Imperative. You have to have those pool vehicles because then people can say, I'll just walk to work and if I have an off-site meeting, I know I have a resource for that."

KENNER KINGSTON
Arch Nexus

stations with a total of four chargers there. Two of the chargers are designated for the company EVs; the other two are reserved for employees who drive their own EVs to work. These stalls are considered the "best" parking spaces, sending a message about the company's priorities.

Initially, some Sacramento staff were concerned about moving from a less urban location with plenty of parking to a rather densely developed part of town where on-site parking is severely limited. The public transportation stipend helps offset any additional costs, and today

many Arch Nexus employees bike, walk, or take public transportation to work.

Although the R Street District is already a highly walkable, bike-friendly neighborhood, Arch Nexus has taken several steps to further support human-powered transportation in the community. The firm sent an advocacy letter to Sacramento's Director of Public Works and contributes to several key neighborhood organizations such as Metro Edge, the R Street Sacramento Partnership, and the Downtown Sacramento Partnership.

SACRAMENTO'S TRANSPORTATION INITIATIVES

The transportation sector is Sacramento's largest source of carbon emissions. The City has taken a multi-pronged approach to reducing both miles driven and the amount of time spent in vehicles, while at the same time improving quality of life. Many of the City's efforts received a boost in 2017, when Sacramento was named the first "Green City" as part of the Electrify America program. This program was created as part of the settlement agreement between Volkswagen Corporation and several entities.

Over ten years, Electrify America will invest $2 billion on infrastructure, education, and access to zero-emissions vehicles, or ZEVs. Of this total, $44 million will be spent in Sacramento, which will use the funding to enhance existing programs and launch new ones.

CAR SHARING: Sacramento boasts four car-sharing programs, three of which use ZEVs exclusively. Through GIG, users can pick up an all-electric Chevy Bolt and drop it off anywhere in the GIG service area. The Community Car Share program, operated by ZipCar, offers two ZEVz and free charging within each participating community, all of which are low-income housing developments.

ELECTRIC BIKES AND SCOOTERS: Sacramento residents also have access to hundreds of electric bicycles and electric scooters through JUMP, a subsidiary of Uber. In June of 2019, Sacramento issued a permit allowing JUMP to double its fleet. At least 20 percent of the EVs must be located in "Opportunity Areas," or low-income neighborhoods.

CHARGING INFRASTRUCTURE: The City is expanding its charging infrastructure. In addition to providing free charging at city-owned parking garages, a new program will encourage EV use by providing curbside charging stations along select streets.

ELECTRIC SHUTTLE: A new shuttle service will utilize twelve electric buses to carry passengers between Davis and Sacramento, starting in 2020. The service will provide up to 400,000 rides in its first year.

THE WATER PETAL

Responding to Nature's Cycles

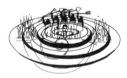

The Water Petal: **RESPONDING TO NATURE'S CYCLES**

THE WATER PETAL
LIVING BUILDING CHALLENGE VERSION 3.0

PETAL INTENT

The intent of the Water Petal is to realign how people use water and to redefine 'waste' in the built environment, so that water is respected as a precious resource. Scarcity of potable water is quickly becoming a serious issue as many countries around the world face severe shortages and compromised water quality. Even regions that have avoided the majority of these problems to date due to a historical presence of abundant fresh water are at risk: the impacts of climate change, highly unsustainable water use patterns, and the continued drawdown of major aquifers portend significant problems ahead.

PETAL IMPERATIVES

• Net Positive Water

The building's water systems are adapted to Sacramento's climate, which is characterized by winter rains and summer drought.

In developed countries, it is all too easy to take clean, abundant water for granted. But the days of using drinking water for flushing toilets may be numbered. Recognizing the converging factors of climate change, unsustainable water use patterns, and the drawdown of major aquifers, the Living Building Challenge Standard notes that water security is quickly becoming a serious issue, even in regions that have historically enjoyed an abundance of fresh water.

This issue was especially poignant for the Arch Nexus team, which was contemplating a Living Building Challenge project for a drought-prone region suffering one of the driest periods on record. When Arch Nexus embarked on the Sacramento regeneration project, they recognized that the ongoing drought in California had pushed water conservation to the forefront, especially among government agencies. They hoped to leverage the drought and promote alternatives to centralized systems which typically only refer to two types of water in buildings: drinking water and wastewater.

Any excess rainwater overflows to a basin surrounding the cisterns.

Imperative 04: Net Positive Water simply states that "one hundred percent of the project's water needs must be supplied by captured precipitation or other natural closed loop water systems, and/or by recycling used project water, and must be purified as needed without the use of chemicals." In addition, all stormwater and water discharge, which includes greywater and "blackwater" from toilets, must be treated and managed on-site.

There is a regulatory pathway for such systems written into the International Building Code and other codes based on the "I-codes." An Alternative Materials and Methods Request, or AMMR, allows a project team to choose solutions that are outside the prescriptive path, so long as they can prove that the materials and methods satisfy the intent of the code.

Arch Nexus engaged Mark Buehrer, a civil engineer and founder and director of 2020 ENGINEERING, to help design the water

systems for the building. Buehrer has designed on-site systems for projects, including Living Buildings, located around the United States, Canada and other countries. He champions systems that capture a forgotten resource—the nutrients in greywater, urine, and human waste—and creates closed-loop systems that not only collect, use, and treat water on-site, but that are part of urban agriculture systems. Such systems confront several issues at once: food security, water security, energy use, and the sustainability of local economies.

The team was greatly informed by their pre-design trip to Seattle where they toured the Bullitt Center and Bertschi School Science Wing, Living Buildings which include water systems designed by 2020 ENGINEERING. Both of these Living Buildings utilize composting toilets and have installed rainwater-to-potable systems. The Bullitt Center directs greywater to a

recirculating constructed wetland for treatment; the water is
then used for irrigation in landscapes outside of the building.
The Bertschi School uses greywater to irrigate an interior "green
wall." The plants in this wall take up greywater through their
roots and evapo-transpire the excess through their leaves. This
elegant living system ensures the building does not discharge
any wastewater.

Arch Nexus Principal Jeff Davis worked with 2020 ENGINEERING
and the regulatory agencies to secure permits. Davis hoped to
gain approval for three innovative systems: composting toilets,
a greywater system, and a "rainwater-to-potable" system that
treats captured rainwater to the standards of drinking water.
Acquiring permits for the first two turned out to be surprisingly
easy, but the rainwater-to-potable system was a different story.

*"Basically the food that you ate yesterday is
processed through your body and becomes
fertilizer for your food next week."*

MARK BUEHRER
2020 ENGINEERING

*"The building code has in it a provision that
if there is something that the code doesn't
cover and you can show that it meets the
intent of the code, it's up to the code official
to make a determination about whether that
can be allowed or not."*

JEFF DAVIS
Arch Nexus

"This is our first project where we implemented rainwater harvesting. It's interesting that our first project is the one that goes all the way. I think that's just Nexus; that's just how we roll. When we're ready to learn something, we're ready to go all the way."

KENNER KINGSTON
Arch Nexus

CAPTURING RAIN

Arch Nexus wanted to use captured rainwater for all indoor uses except for toilet and urinal flushing, which would rely on treated greywater.

And since greywater was not going to be used to irrigate landscaping due to regulatory hurdles, they wanted to use captured rainwater for outdoor irrigation as well. They would have to size the cisterns accordingly so that they would have an adequate supply throughout the year.

Sacramento receives an average of 18.51 inches of rain annually. Interestingly, this is very close to the average annual rainfall in Salt Lake City; however, the pattern of rainfall is much different. Whereas Salt Lake City receives rain and snow throughout the year, the Central Valley's climate is characterized by summer drought; in fact, it is typical for Sacramento to receive no rain for four months or more. At the same time, water demand would be higher in summer. Not only would more employees be bicycling to work and showering there, the landscaping would require more irrigation water. With no new influx of supply, the cistern levels would be steadily dropping until the fall rains came.

2020 ENGINEERING developed an annual water budget which was based on their estimation of how much water could be captured each month. They took into account not only the building roof area and average monthly precipitation values, but the pattern of precipitation and how full the cisterns were likely to be at any given time.

Next, 2020 ENGINEERING estimated demand from both landscaping plants and potable water use inside the building. Landscape Architect Heather Olson worked with 2020

ENGINEERING to create water budgets for several urban agriculture scenarios. Arch Nexus had data from their Salt Lake City office to help estimate indoor water demand for the Sacramento office. Taking all of these factors into account, 2020 ENGINEERING recommended three five thousand-gallon cisterns, for a total capacity of fifteen thousand gallons. They estimated that captured rainwater would be divided almost evenly between indoor (potable) use and outdoor irrigation.

Stormwater would also have to be taken into account. The first flush of any rain event would not be captured in the cisterns and so would need to be treated as stormwater. In addition, any rain

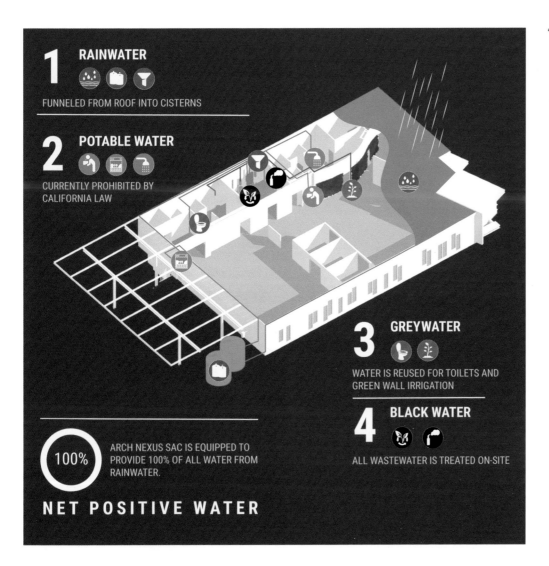

1 RAINWATER

FUNNELED FROM ROOF INTO CISTERNS

2 POTABLE WATER

CURRENTLY PROHIBITED BY
CALIFORNIA LAW

3 GREYWATER

WATER IS REUSED FOR TOILETS AND
GREEN WALL IRRIGATION

4 BLACK WATER

ALL WASTEWATER IS TREATED ON-SITE

100% ARCH NEXUS SAC IS EQUIPPED TO
PROVIDE 100% OF ALL WATER FROM
RAINWATER.

NET POSITIVE WATER

"Our Salt Lake City office is literally the greenest building in the Intermountain West, and that building wastes so much water you can't even believe it. So these conversations are starting to happen and we're trying to figure out how to fix that problem, because that building is ten years old now."

KENNER KINGSTON
Arch Nexus

that fell on the roof when the cisterns were full needed to be treated on site and returned to the river cleaner than when it fell as rain.

Warren Consulting designed the stormwater system. The high water table precludes stormwater from infiltrating into the ground; for this reason, they did not design infiltration basins for the site. Instead, excess stormwater (which has already flowed through the vortex filter) spills into a basin surrounding the cisterns. From there it is filtered through a sand/oil interceptor. The interceptor treats stormwater by allowing oil and other pollutants that are lighter than water float to the top of the tank, while sand and other heavy substances sink.

The cleaned stormwater then flows into the City's stormwater system, which directs the flow back into creeks and rivers. Because it has been treated by the vortex filter and sand/oil interceptor, any stormwater that leaves Arch Nexus SAC is cleaner than it was when it first fell onto the site.

Although the parking area consists of impervious concrete, a trench drain in the strip between the parking area and the alley collects stormwater and directs it to the oil/sand interceptor. In addition, permeable planted areas help slow the flow of stormwater.

The Water Petal: **RESPONDING TO NATURE'S CYCLES**

A REGULATORY SNAFU

While the City of Sacramento was very receptive to the greywater and composting toilet systems, they felt that the rainwater-to-potable system was out of their jurisdiction and referred Davis to the county. The county, in turn, deferred to the state.

"We have inevitability on our side. There will be another tragic drought. And when there is, we'll be ready with all the data when the Water Board is ready to listen."

KENNER KINGSTON
Arch Nexus

When Davis first approached the California State Water Resources Control Board with plans for the rainwater-to-potable system, the staff member he worked with was enthusiastic about what Arch Nexus was trying to achieve and began coaching Davis through the process.

In spring of 2016, the state requested an evaluation of the system to be conducted by a third party. 2020 ENGINEERING helped Arch Nexus find someone to conduct the evaluation and write a report, which Davis submitted.

64

Around this same time, without warning or explanation, the person with whom Davis had been working was no longer available. In his place, Davis began receiving official, impersonal, and delayed responses.

As it turned out, Arch Nexus was attempting to gain approval for an experimental system at exactly the wrong time, drought or no drought.

The California state legislature was preparing to pass a new regulation in fall of 2016 which limited the number of small water districts in the state. SB 1263 was crafted in response to a host of new developments that had sprung up in recent years. The bill discouraged these new developments from forming their own water districts and instead encouraged them to tie into existing ones. The state's argument was that newer, smaller water districts did not have the resources to safeguard drinking water the way larger public districts could. While the bill was aimed at protecting water supplies, it all but guaranteed that Arch Nexus would not receive approval for their system.

In fact, Arch Nexus received neither an approval nor a denial after submitting the evaluation report; instead, the Water Board kept them in regulatory limbo. As construction continued, they had to make a decision about whether to install the treatment system or not.

Kingston was fairly certain the system would not be approved, but he decided to emulate the Bullitt Center and install the equipment anyway, with the hope that the regulatory climate would soon change. (The Bullitt Center, a building located in Seattle, Washington, earned full Living Building certification even though they were not allowed to operate the rainwater-to-potable system. The project used an exemption credit for designing and seeking permit approval for a potable rainwater system. Of note, the Bullitt Center system has since been approved for potable water use of its collected rainwater.)

The building inspector wanted clarity on the issue before he would issue the temporary Certificate of Occupancy for Arch Nexus SAC. Davis began pressing the Water Board for an answer. Right before the winter holidays, and just days before Arch Nexus was supposed to move into the renovated building, Davis received a letter. But the letter was not a denial, as expected. Instead, the state was requesting another study.

Kingston, in his company's application for the International Living Future Institute, argued that this request was tantamount to a denial. Not only would another study be costly, both in terms of time and money, there was no guarantee that they would receive a final decision afterwards—or a request for yet another study. ILFI agreed that Arch Nexus had satisfied the spirit of the Imperative. Arch Nexus moved into their new office, and while landscaping is irrigated with rainwater, employees use municipal water inside the building for fixtures that require potable water. The micro-flush vacuum toilets and urinal use treated greywater, and the Living Wall is irrigated with greywater.

But that is not the end of the story.

As per federal law, any entity that operates a potable water system for sixty days or more must become a public water district. Sometime soon, Arch Nexus intends to run and test the rainwater-to-potable system for fifty-nine days. They will not let anyone drink or even use the water, but they will hire a third-party agency to test it. This way, they will be able to present their data, which will hopefully prove that the water is safe, to the Water Board. Meanwhile, the filtration system is installed but deactivated, and stubs for the third cistern are already in place.

RAINWATER IN MOTION

When rainwater falls onto the roof, it flows through a downspout screen and into a vortex filter which uses a vertical filter element to remove debris. From there water flows into one of two five thousand-gallon cisterns. The cisterns are a highly visible aspect of the rainwater system, occupying a prominent position at the northeast corner of the building.

Before being treated further, rainwater is available to the drip irrigation system and to the greywater day tank, which calls for make-up water if it is less than half full. Careful plant selection and efficient irrigation equipment help ensure that the urban agriculture landscape can be irrigated with collected rainfall alone.

The rainwater-to-potable system is ready to create drinking water. It consists of a series of treatment systems, including a slow sand filter, a five-micron carbon filter, and a UV disinfection unit. The technology is fairly standard, and 2020 ENGINEERING and Arch Nexus are confident that it can reliably produce safe, clean potable water. All they need is a permit to begin using the treated rainwater in the building's potable water fixtures.

66

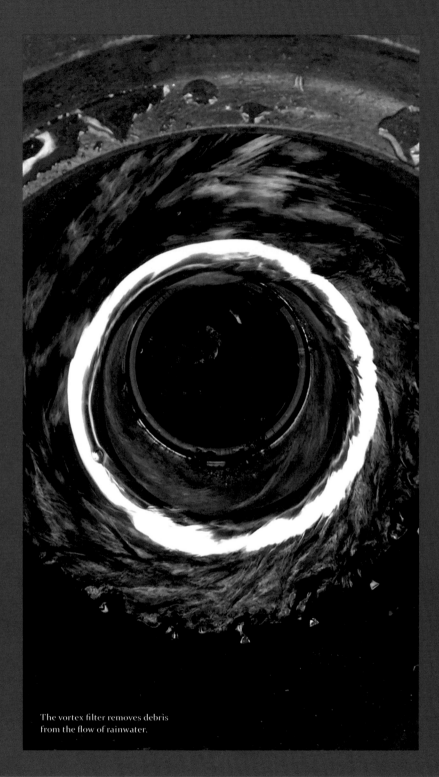

The vortex filter removes debris
from the flow of rainwater.

A GREEN SOLUTION FOR GREYWATER

2020 ENGINEERING knew that few things can delay a Living Building Challenge project like waiting for a permit.

For example, at the Bullitt Center, acquiring a permit for the constructed wetland greywater treatment system and for the reuse of treated greywater in outdoor landscaping took eighteen months. To ease the regulatory process, 2020 ENGINEERING recommended that Arch Nexus keep all greywater use inside the building. Using greywater to irrigate landscaping plants outdoors would trigger a permitting process with the Department of Health, whereas indoor greywater use falls exclusively under the jurisdiction of the Plumbing Department as part of the building permit process.

Keeping all greywater uses inside the building would have other advantages. In the controlled indoor environment, they would not have to contend nearly as much with varying humidity and soil moisture conditions as they would if they were using greywater to irrigate outdoor plantings. They could also control the amount of airflow over vertical walls of plantings, which they were considering to evaporate 100 percent of the excess greywater.

In California, greywater may be used to flush toilets. As per Chapter 15 in the 2016 California Plumbing Code, it must be filtered and disinfected and meet minimum water quality standards. The plumbing must be kept separate from the potable system, and both systems must be independently tested to ensure there is no cross-connection.

Since the Jets vacuum flush toilets require a very small amount of water (about one pint) per flush, using greywater rather than potable, or drinking water as the supply was an obvious solution. Before proceeding, 2020 ENGINEERING needed to calculate how much greywater building occupants would produce and match that amount with demand. Arch Nexus had the benefit of data from their Salt Lake City office about how often employees bicycled to work and used the office's shower facilities. They knew more people would likely choose to commute by bicycle

in Sacramento because it is so flat. They used the Salt Lake City data to create models which estimated the amount of greywater that would be generated in Sacramento and compared this volume to predicted daily demand for greywater from the vacuum-flush toilets. They were not surprised to learn that occupants would likely be generating more greywater than could be used by the toilets alone. They needed a path for this excess.

The team had been attracted to the Green Wall at the Bertschi School Science Wing, which uses live plants to evaporate excess greywater, and Buehrer assured them that such a solution would

The Water Petal: **RESPONDING TO NATURE'S CYCLES**

68

NO ONE EVER
INJURED THEIR
EYESIGHT
BY
LOOKING ON
THE

REGENERATIVE RETROFIT: *California's First Living Building*

work well in Sacramento. The Green Wall at the Bertschi School functions even during Seattle winters, with its short days, cloudy skies, and high humidities. The drier, sunnier Sacramento climate would be much more amenable to high evaporation rates.

The team loved the idea of growing food plants on several indoor walls and using nutrient-rich greywater to feed them, but the potential issues—pollen allergies, and how to ensure fruit-bearing plants were pollinated without using bees, for example—convinced them to come up with an alternative.

President Kenner Kingston took inspiration from Fern Canyon, a spectacular creek canyon on the Northern California coast with vertical walls which support an abundance of ferns. With this vision, they conceived a Living Wall of plants that would utilize excess greywater, extract its nutrients, and bring beauty and life into the building.

The wall would need to be sized and plants carefully selected. Unlike most landscaping plants, which in drought-prone climates a preference for those that minimize evaporative water loss, the plants for the Living Wall needed to evaporate water—the more, the better. In addition, the plants would need to thrive in the challenging light conditions.

Arch Nexus Landscape Architect Jennifer Styduhar worked with David Brenner of Habitat Horticulture on the design of the Living Wall. This company specializes in vertical gardens that are supported with a lightweight structure, fabric "pockets," and soilless growing medium. They chose several fern varieties, striving for a combination of colors and textures that captured the essence of Fern Canyon.

"We had to make sure that Living Wall in the middle of winter could still move that water through the plants and exhaust out the building. Because of our experience at the Bertschi School, we felt confident to take a similar approach with Arch Nexus."

MARK BUEHRER
2020 ENGINEERING

"Once we told them how many square feet the Living Wall had to be, it took on that creative curving look, which to me is the hallmark design component of the building. It's the first thing you see when you come through the building, and you can see it from all the workstations."

MARK BUEHRER
2020 ENGINEERING

The design team considered lighting the Living Wall from above with skylights. This was an attractive solution that ensured the building would still meet the net-positive energy goal. However, daylighting would cut into the roof area available for solar modules; besides, skylights are designed to deliver diffused rather than direct light, which could introduce unwanted solar heat gain. Habitat Horticulture was also concerned that daylighting alone would not provide enough vertical illuminance for the entire wall and advised using LED "grow lights" instead. Ultimately, they settled on highly efficient LED lights, which can be "tuned" for the light requirements of specific plants. The lights are mounted on the ceiling about three feet away from the Living Wall and angled so that light reaches all of the plants. The lights are programmed to turn on for twelve hours in the evening, starting at 5:00 pm. Because the wall is illuminated, people can see it from outside the building at night.

69

THE ARCH NEXUS SAC GREYWATER SYSTEM

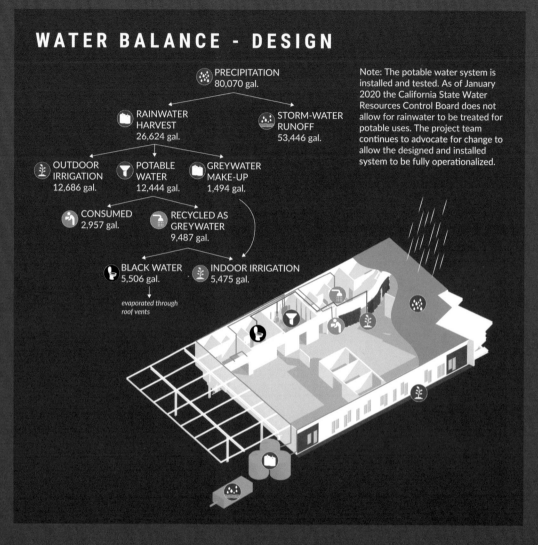

WATER BALANCE - DESIGN

PRECIPITATION
80,070 gal.

RAINWATER HARVEST
26,624 gal.

STORM-WATER RUNOFF
53,446 gal.

OUTDOOR IRRIGATION
12,686 gal.

POTABLE WATER
12,444 gal.

GREYWATER MAKE-UP
1,494 gal.

CONSUMED
2,957 gal.

RECYCLED AS GREYWATER
9,487 gal.

BLACK WATER
5,506 gal.

evaporated through roof vents

INDOOR IRRIGATION
5,475 gal.

Note: The potable water system is installed and tested. As of January 2020 the California State Water Resources Control Board does not allow for rainwater to be treated for potable uses. The project team continues to advocate for change to allow the designed and installed system to be fully operationalized.

The greywater system collects "used" water from bathroom sinks, showers, and from the sink and dishwasher in the break room. Greywater drains into a submersible pump in the floor; from there, it is pumped through a roughing filter, slow sand filter, and 5-micron carbon filter before being disinfected with UV light. Treated greywater is stored in a day tank and used to flush toilets and feed the Living Wall. If the level in the greywater day tank falls below forty-five gallons, it is topped off with rainwater from one of the cisterns. This happens more frequently in winter, when fewer people are bicycling to work. The system is connected to the sanitary sewer, as required, but this connection has never been used.

The Living Wall is broken into two sections; together, it measures ten feet tall by thirty feet long. A drip system across the top of the wall draws greywater from the day tank at least twice per day. Over the course of ten to fifteen minutes, treated greywater drips down the length of wall and percolates into the plant medium. Any excess drains into a tray at the bottom of the wall and recirculates back into the day tank. Plants on the wall can absorb between three to six gallons per day. The drip system runs on a timed schedule, but Erica McBride, the building manager, can adjust it if she feels the plants need more water. Moisture and oxygen are released from the plants into the occupied space, improving indoor air quality.

"Interestingly enough, our prediction that local jurisdictional authorities would be more amenable to unusual systems was accurate. Not that permitting was easy, but we got the greywater and composting systems permitted."

KENNER KINGSTON
Arch Nexus

"Usually you're trying to design landscaping to use as little water as possible. We had the opposite problem: design as small a wall as possible to evaporate as much water as possible."

MARK BUEHRER
2020 ENGINEERING

WASTE AS A RESOURCE: THE COMPOSTING SYSTEM

From the beginning the design team determined to use composting toilets in their building.

Composting toilets not only greatly reduce the use of water, they eliminate the problem of "blackwater," or water contaminated with human waste, by keeping it separate from other "used" water. Composting toilets create a closed-loop system which enables the nutrients to be safely captured and transformed into a finished product that can be used to nourish plants. Meanwhile, greywater from sinks and showers can be easily treated and used elsewhere inside or outside a building.

Although composting toilets are certainly unusual in office buildings, the Bullitt Center in Seattle had broken ground by becoming the first six-story commercial building to rely on them exclusively. The foam-flush toilets in this building rely on gravity to transport waste to composters in the basement. But Arch Nexus SAC was a one-story building with no basement. The design team explored the possibility of excavating a basement so they could locate the composting units below the toilets, but this solution was cost prohibitive. Instead, they turned to vacuum flush toilets supplied by a Norwegian company, Jets Group. Identical to the toilets found on cruise ships, vacuum-flush toilets use air suction to transport material to the composters. A "vacummmerator" pump, which includes a macerator, creates the vacuum, breaks down the waste, and pumps the slurry to its destination.

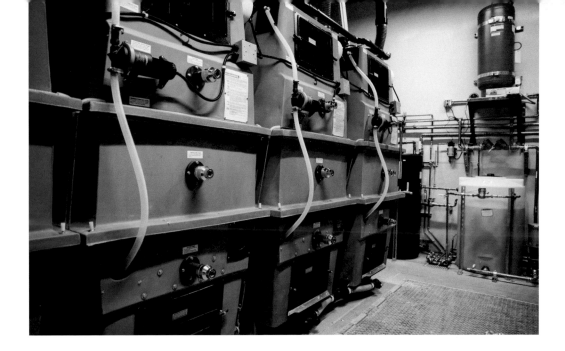

The composting system at Arch Nexus SAC includes eight composter units that receive waste from highly efficient vacuum flush toilets.

Vacuum flush toilets require about one pint of water per flush, a fraction of that used by an ultra-low flow toilet but significantly more than a foam-flush toilet, which only requires about one cup of water per flush. The composters can only receive between four and five gallons of liquid per day and still perform optimally. Hence, using the Jets toilets would increase the total number of composting units required. Although adding more composters would also add some cost, it was a much less expensive option than excavating a new basement.

As with the greywater system, the composting toilets also required an AMMR for permit approval. The City of Sacramento ultimately approved the system but required the building to be connected to the city's sanitary sewer in case of emergency overflow. Since the building already had an existing sewer connection, this did not add any cost.

The Arch Nexus SAC office includes two restrooms. Each relies on a dedicated vacummerator pump to transport waste to a bank of eight composters. A manifold diverts output evenly among the units, with a slug of waste directed to one of the composters during each flush.

The Phoenix composters are provided by Advanced Composting Systems LLC, the same company that supplied the Bullitt Center. The units use an aerobic process to break down human waste,

transforming it into a mulch product that can safely be used on landscaping plants.

The composters require dry and wet cycles to function optimally. Each composter comes equipped with a fan to evaporate moisture and a pump which conveys leachate, the liquid which seeps out of the compost, from the bottom of the unit to the top. Any excess moisture drains from the units into a common leachate tank. When the composters need extra liquid, building manager Erica McBride uses a portable pump to transfer liquid from the leachate tank back into composters, where it is sprayed evenly across the top. This tank is connected to Sacramento's sanitary sewer, as required by the city. McBride also adds a five-gallon bucket of wood chips to each composter every other week and aerates the material using a hand-cranked auger.

As new material enters the composters, older material makes its way to the bottom of the units. At the time of print McBride has not yet harvested the fully composted mulch, as the system is oversized for the current number of occupants. However, the product has been tested and meets U.S. EPA Class B compost standards, which means it can be applied as fertilizer on private property, so long as the plants or their fruits are not intended for human consumption. Because most of the plantings on the Arch Nexus site are edible, they will likely offer the compost to Arch Nexus employees to use on their own properties.

THE ENERGY PETAL

Engaged Occupants in
a High-Performance Building

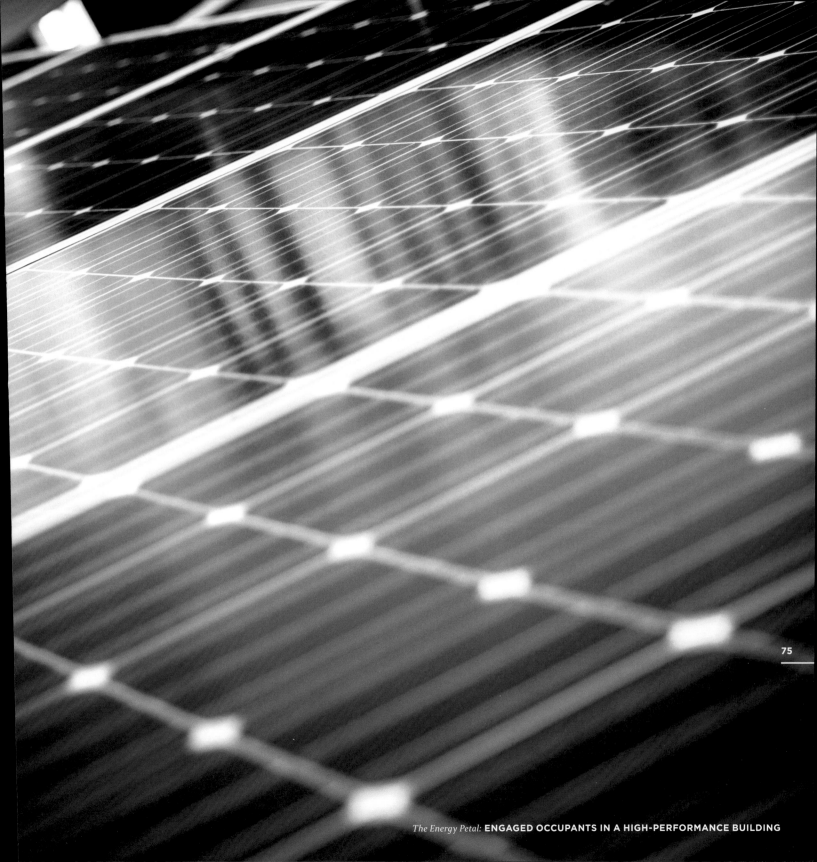

The Energy Petal: **ENGAGED OCCUPANTS IN A HIGH-PERFORMANCE BUILDING**

THE ENERGY PETAL
LIVING BUILDING CHALLENGE VERSION 3.0

PETAL INTENT

The intent of the Energy Petal is to signal a new age of design, wherein the built environment relies solely on renewable forms of energy and operates year round in a safe, pollution-free manner. In addition, it aims to prioritize reductions and optimization before technological solutions are applied to eliminate wasteful spending—of energy, resources, and dollars. The majority of energy generated today is from highly polluting and often politically destabilizing sources including coal, gas, oil and nuclear power. Large-scale hydro, while inherently cleaner, results in widespread damage to ecosystems. Burning wood, trash or pellets releases particulates and carbon dioxide (CO_2) into the atmosphere and often strains local supplies of sustainably harvested biomass while robbing the soil of much-needed nutrient recycling. The effects of these energy sources on regional and planetary health are becoming increasingly evident through climate change, the most worrisome major global trend attributed to human activity.

PETAL IMPERATIVE
• Net Positive Energy

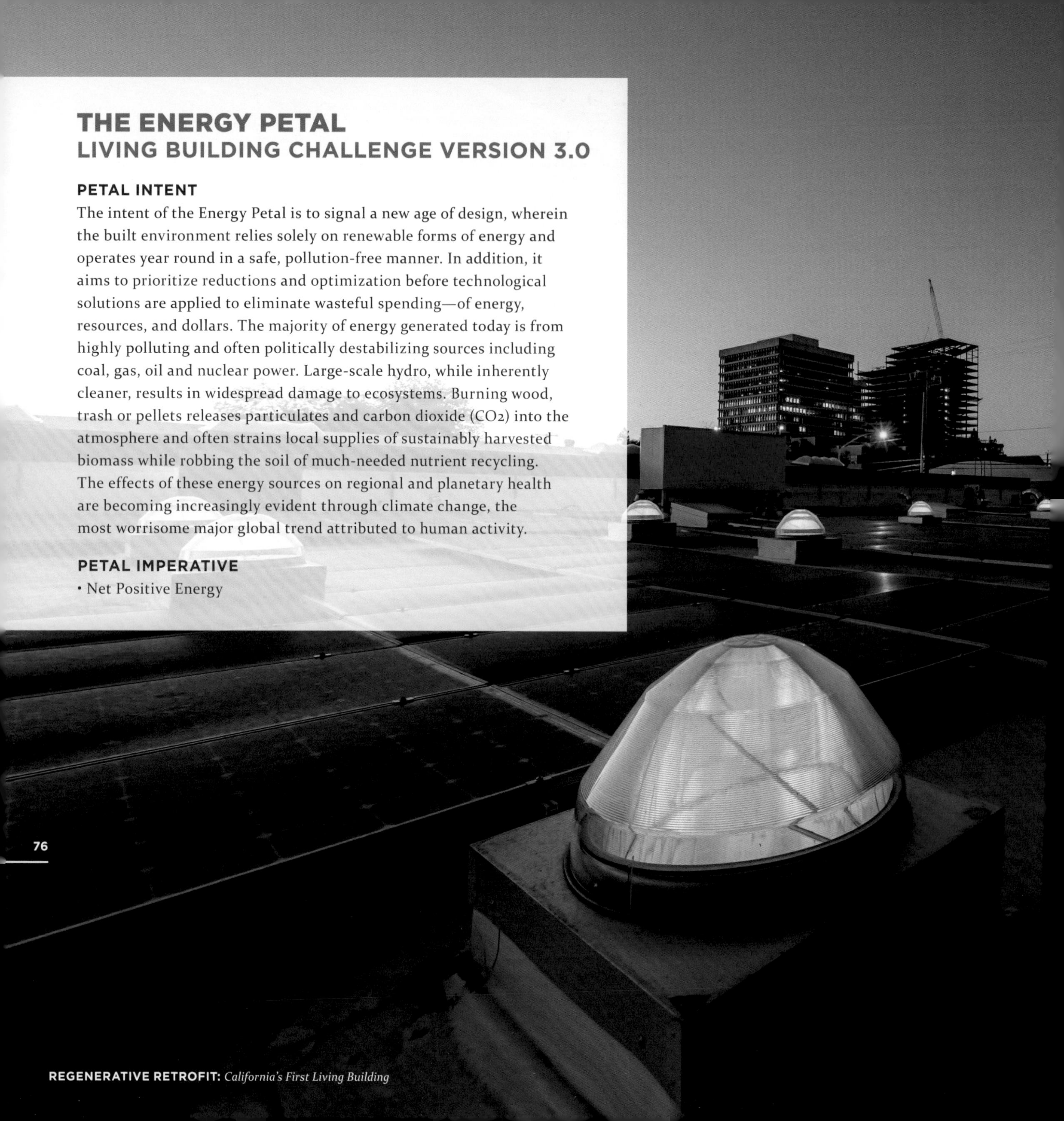

Solatubes, which harvest daylight for the building's interior, share space with solar PV modules on the roof of Arch Nexus SAC.

Together, residential and commercial buildings represent 40 percent of the United States' energy use and are responsible for one-third of our greenhouse gas emissions. By designing, building, and renovating energy-efficient structures, building professionals play a vital role in impacting energy use for decades to come.

The opportunity to transform existing buildings into models of efficiency is often eclipsed by the glamor of new ones. But although the existing building stock is slowly being replaced by those built to today's more stringent energy codes, many buildings that are operating today will still be standing (and wasting energy) ten, twenty, or thirty years from now. Retrofitting an older building not only saves energy for the rest of the building's life, it may conserve significant embodied energy if construction of a new one is avoided. It was with this understanding that Arch Nexus undertook transforming a fifty-year-old warehouse into a Living Building.

77

The salt water batteries provide a measure of resilience during power outages, and they do not contain any toxic materials.

Net Positive Energy, the single Imperative under the Energy Petal, simply states that one hundred and five percent of the project's energy needs must be supplied by on-site renewable energy on a net annual basis, without the use of on-site combustion. In addition, projects must provide back-up energy storage for emergency lighting and refrigeration. This represents an evolution from previous iterations of the Standard, which required a building to achieve net-zero energy and did not require any on-site storage.

A net-positive energy building is itself a lofty goal; in this case, the design team also had to work within the constraints of the existing building, including its orientation, general form and

footprint, and its proximity to several large trees, which would interfere with on-site solar generation.

Arch Nexus had already successfully overhauled a fifty-year-old building in Salt Lake City, creating an energy-efficient and comfortable space that uses half the energy of a comparable office building. They understood that the key to optimizing energy efficiency measures is having knowledgeable occupants who understand their role in energy performance and who are willing to do their part to reduce energy consumption. They believed they could achieve net-positive energy at Arch Nexus SAC through a combination of active and passive measures paired with robust occupant engagement.

MODELING FOR
NET-POSITIVE ENERGY

Energy modeling is key to designing a high-performance building.

The typical approach entails creating a baseline model that incorporates the values prescribed by code for each category—window u-values, or the air leakage rate through the building envelope, for example. These can be changed to see how they impact overall energy performance compared to the baseline; different scenarios are used to weigh the cost of each improvement against its benefit. Put another way, the model is used to run cost-to-benefit analyses to determine which measures yield the most energy savings for the least cost.

The Arch Nexus SAC team approached energy modeling for their Sacramento project differently. From the outset, they knew that the goal was not to achieve a minimum threshold for energy use, but to create a building that used as little energy as possible, given the budget constraints. Whatever energy the building consumed would have to be more than offset by solar energy. With this in mind, the team did not employ a baseline model. Instead, they chose the most efficient options enabled by the budget, and strove to create as accurate a model as possible.

Many factors go into energy modeling: climate and weather, details about the building envelope, and its shape and orientation, to name just a few. Building schedules are a key element. These schedules reflect how occupants use the building: how many hours lights are on every day, heating and cooling set points during business hours, and so on. But the schedules employed in energy models are often not realistic and in fact tend to be optimistic. This

is why such models frequently underestimate actual energy use.

Because the Living Building Challenge is a performance-based program, an overly optimistic energy model could have serious consequences, potentially costing the building its net zero energy certification.

"Energy modeling gets real very quickly," says Kingston. "We didn't want conservative schedules, and we didn't want liberal schedules. We wanted accurate schedules." Arch Nexus surveyed each member of the firm at both the Salt Lake City and Sacramento offices so they could create fine-grained realistic schedules for occupancy, lighting, and HVAC use. These surveys also helped guide their occupant training program.

The Engineering consultant used a tool called eQUEST (Quick Energy Simulation Tool) to perform energy modeling. Their model predicted an Energy Use Intensity (EUI) of 36 kBtu per square foot per year—less than half of the national average for a small office building. The building's actual EUI would turn out to be just over 26, significantly lower than predicted.

"When there's a major earthquake and every other office in Sac isn't functioning, we'll be running. We're not just resilient because of our batteries, but because our IT backbone is also resilient."

KENNER KINGSTON
Arch Nexus

79

Dynamic shadows from the London Planetrees play against the subtly shaded metal panels on the building's exterior.

REGENERATIVE RETROFIT: *California's First Living Building*

SHADOWS AND SUNLIGHT

When Kenner Kingston, Joe Yee, and Charlie Downs were initially searching for property and visited the warehouse on 10th Street, one of the first things they did was ascend to the roof and study the solar opportunity. Soon after, Brian Cassil performed some preliminary daylight simulations.

The existing trees lining 10th Street were both an asset and an issue. In addition to their inherent loveliness, the trees were valuable for reducing solar heat gain and glare.

But for a good part of every day, the trees shaded the east side of the building and about one-half of the roof, which would impact solar energy production and severely inhibit daylighting. The degree of shading varied throughout the day and through the seasons, adding an extra variable to Cassil's daylighting analyses. In spite of the challenges presented by the London Planetrees, Cassil determined that carefully designed top lighting for daylight would be the best strategy.

Arch Nexus understood the value of natural daylighting to occupants from their experience with their office in Salt Lake City, where Cassil had first performed daylight studies for the firm. There Arch Nexus employed tubular skylights called Solatubes to illuminate a second-story office space that was originally conceived as overflow work space. Daylighting helped create such a pleasant work environment that this space became known as The Loft.

Cassil had learned two important lessons from the Salt Lake City project and from post-occupancy studies performed there and for other buildings. First, daylight sensors often do not work as advertised. They are supposed to tune to the level of ambient natural light, but Cassil found that all too often, they respond poorly or not at all.

The second insight was that the recommended interior illumination levels prescribed by the Illuminating Engineering Society (IES) do not necessarily result in successful daylighting. The prescribed levels for an open office space are 300 lux, or lumens per square meter, if that space does not include individual task lighting. For an open office with task lighting, the recommended level is just 50 lux. LEED guidelines recommend 300 lux across the board. Cassil suspected that the 300 lux level was unnecessarily high. He performed an experiment at the Salt Lake City office whereby he steadily lowered light levels over a period of time, approaching 50 lux in the darkest areas in the space. After a few weeks, he polled staff about the lighting conditions. He found that people were satisfied with levels down to 100 lux, but that levels much below that were perceived as too dim, even when they had individual task lights.

Cassil applied these lessons to the Arch Nexus SAC project. His goal was to use daylighting wherever and whenever possible and to reduce the reliance on artificial lighting. First, he decided that although the lighting system would include daylight sensors, the Arch Nexus SAC office would mostly rely on humans to make decisions about when to dim or turn off artificial lights. Secondly, he decided to use an illumination threshold of at least 100 lux.

The design ensures that all regularly occupied spaces can be lit with natural light at least four hours per day. This Cassil accomplished with Solatubes, which had been so successful in Salt Lake City. These tubular skylights use a highly efficient reflector and diffuser to harvest sunlight and bring it deep within a space. The reflectance of interior surfaces, including ceilings, walls, and furniture, was also increased to enhance daylighting. All artificial lighting is LED, and all workstations include individual task lights.

81

AN ENHANCED BUILDING ENVELOPE

The building envelope was the only portion of the existing building that was already optimized for its cost to benefit. The team determined that the existing portion of the building envelope only required minor enhancement. However, the roof would need a complete overhaul.

The existing roof was lightly framed, and it had to be re-engineered to comply with seismic requirements and so it could support solar panels, HVAC equipment, and skylights. Steel c-channels were added to reinforce the existing glu-lam beams, and dimensional lumber was added to reinforce some of the purlins. The roof was insulated with a minimum of four inches of polyisocyanurate sandwiched between two layers of sheathing and coated with a high-reflectance TPO, or white thermoplastic. This material reflects solar radiation, reducing cooling loads in the summer. Code requires a reflectance of at least 0.37, or 63 percent; the new roof has a reflectance of 78 percent.

The walls are a hybrid of existing and new materials. The original existing 2x6 wood framing is sheathed with plywood. Cavities are filled with existing batt insulation, and the walls are newly sealed with the Prosoco weather barrier system. Two inches of new rigid insulation provide a thermal break and enhance the cavity insulation. New metal panels are installed into the framing through the rigid insulation.

Glazing is one of the most important elements of a building, affecting not only energy performance, but occupant comfort, daylighting, and aesthetics. In this case, the arrangement and shapes of the windows work in tandem with the metal panels to evoke the "Reeds and Rails" theme of the exterior, and the glass-fronted design lab and entry send a message of transparency and welcoming to the community.

Most highly efficient buildings have proportionately fewer windows—a concept often expressed as the Window-to-Wall Ratio, which is a measure of the percentage of glazing compared to the total wall area. Though a lower WWR generally translates to a more efficient envelope, this must be balanced with other considerations, such as providing occupants with views, daylighting, and access to fresh air through the use of operable windows.

The team prioritized glazing around the new entry and design lab. Windows on the east façade provide views and contribute to the exterior aesthetic, but they do not contribute significantly to daylighting because of the shading from nearby trees. Windows were not possible on the west side because of the adjacent building. The resulting WWR of 19.4 is well below the baseline of 40 percent established by California's Title 24.

Glazing in the regenerated Arch Nexus SAC building consists of storefront and curtainwall systems for the entry, lobby, and design lab and operable windows in the east and south façades and in the north façade of the lobby. All of these windows are essential for the natural ventilation strategy, as they help draw air through the entire office space. Solatubes bring in light from above and provide most of the daylighting. Operable ventilated skylights were installed in some locations.

All of the window systems use double-paned low-e glazing. The Kawneer storefront and curtainwall systems are designed to limit heat transfer through the aluminum frames. The tilt-and-turn windows from Jeld-Wen are made with aluminum-clad wood frames. These windows can swing in sideways, but they can also tilt inward from the top, allowing for a high degree of control of natural ventilation.

Efficient tilt-and-turn windows can funnel fresh air into the space.

HEATING AND COOLING AN EFFICIENT BUILDING

Heating and cooling often comprises a good percentage of a commercial building's energy use, but in high-performance buildings, these loads are minimized far below the norm.

The plan for Arch Nexus SAC was to take advantage of the city's mild shoulder seasons and use natural ventilation whenever possible. At one point the team considered a solar chimney system that would preclude the need for a mechanical system at all. They also studied a ground-source geothermal heat pump system, but concluded they did not have the space for a geothermal well field outside the building, and that excavating one underneath the existing building was too costly. In the end, Arch Nexus decided on a highly efficient variable refrigerant flow, or VRF system.

VRF systems were first developed by Japanese company Daikin and quickly adopted in Asian and European countries. They have been gaining ground in the United States in recent years, especially for high-performance projects. VRF systems work by utilizing an efficient compressor unit which conditions refrigerant and routes it to any one of several indoor units, or "fan coils." Unlike conventional "on/off" systems, the compressor can modulate its motor speed to demand. Each zone can be set to a different temperature; this way, energy is not wasted heating or cooling a space unnecessarily.

The VRF system selected for the Sacramento project is an air-cooled system, which means the condensers are mounted outside and rely on air movement across a heat exchanger. A dedicated outside air supply fan pulls ventilation air into a plenum, where it is ducted to each of the VRF units. In addition, a double-walled heat exchanger attached to the condensers increases the efficiency of heat rejection and is also used to preheat incoming city water from about 55 degrees to 115 degrees.

Two condensers are mounted on the roof. One serves the main office, which is divided into ten zones, each with its own fan-coil unit. Rooms that are not regularly occupied, such as the restrooms, break room, and janitor's closet, are conditioned using exhaust fans which transfer air under doors or through grilles. The communications room, which houses the office's computer servers, is unlike the rest of the building in that it has a constant heat load. For this reason it is served by a separate, cooling–only condensing unit and fan coil.

To reduce both energy and water consumption, low-flow faucets and showerheads were specified for the bathrooms and break room. These lower energy consumption because less energy is required to heat a smaller volume of water. The fixtures also include occupancy sensors that shut them off automatically when no one is present.

The domestic hot water system includes a highly efficient recirculation pump which reduces water use by returning "unused" hot water back to the water heater in a continuous loop; this way, a user never has to wait for hot water to replace the cold water standing in the pipes. However, the "recirc pump" does use energy when it is running, even during the many evening and weekend hours when the building is not occupied. For this reason, it is programmed to automatically shut off once the security system is armed in the evening.

Thin clients at each workstation use just five watts, whereas a typical desktop computer uses between 300 and 400 watts.

OWNING OFFICE ENERGY DEMAND

Arch Nexus's offices see high computer use. Staff use RAM-heavy modeling programs such as Autodesk Revit, and workstations typically consume around 400 watts for eight or more hours per day.

The design team was determined to cut this usage drastically, so that no workstation ever uses more than 100 watts, including discretionary equipment such as personal cell phone chargers.

Arch Nexus made the unusual decision to locate its computer server locally, within the building. The server represents the greatest single source of plug load energy demand, one they could have easily off-loaded to another building. In the interest of authenticity, they decided to own the load and incorporate it into their building's net-positive energy equation.

Next, they decided to outfit workstations with thin clients, which offload their energy usage to the server. Thin clients use only about five to ten watts apiece, much less than a conventional laptop or desktop computer, because they access programs remotely rather than rely on stored memory. This strategy also concentrates the heat from plug loads into the server room rather than distributing it in the office area. As was mentioned in the previous section, this room is cooled using a dedicated VRF condenser and fan-coil unit.

Hosting the server also enhances the firm's resilience, not only in Sacramento, but in the Salt Lake City office. Computer networks are comprised of many nodes—devices such as a computer or printer, a server, and the Internet itself. Nodes can send and receive information. Creating redundant pathways ensures that a device can always do so, even if a part of the system is "down" and certain nodes are unavailable. Now, devices in either Salt Lake City or Sacramento can route through the Sacramento server; this way, if part of the network is compromised in Salt Lake City, the whole Arch Nexus enterprise can still function.

In addition to the highly efficient thin clients, the team specified Energy Star-rated appliances and office equipment, including copy machines. These appliances use less energy when operating, and some also have built-in features that save energy when they are not in use. In addition, a vampire switch automatically cuts power to all nonessential equipment when the building is unoccupied. Like the recirculating pump, the vampire switch is linked to the security system and eliminates unnecessary loads while the security system is armed.

85

TAPPING THE SUN

Early on, the team determined that, although the trees on 10th Street would make solar production less efficient, they would still be able to generate enough energy to more than offset the building's energy use.

Kingston and Downs liked the notion of "conspicuous sustainability," and originally envisioned a shed roof angling above a row of clerestory windows, which would support solar PV modules and be highly visible from the street. But this element proved too expensive, and they decided to work with the building's flat roof.

As the team moved through Design Development, they struggled with the roof's constraints. Shading from the trees meant that part of the array would not achieve its full potential. In addition, the modules were to be mounted flat, rather than angled toward the sun. Then there was the limited roof area. It needed to accommodate the modules, HVAC equipment and Solatubes; in addition, code required a four foot-wide pathway for firefighter access.

Ultimately, the team determined that the roof would not support enough solar modules to achieve net-positive energy use. They decided to add a canopy on the south side of the building. The canopy would support additional PV panels, and like the trees, it would also reduce solar heat gain and glare. The canopy also became an essential element in creating a sheltered and semi-private break area for staff. Finally, the canopy supports a steel walkway, required for firefighter access, that spans the space between the canopy and the roof, making room for more PV modules on the roof.

Arch Nexus decided to contract with Hunt Electric, a solar provider based in Utah with whom they enjoyed a long history. The 91 kW solar array consists of 305 modules from Oregon manufacturer SolarWorld. The modules are equipped with microinverters which allow each module to perform at its maximum efficiency, even if neighboring modules are shaded or otherwise compromised.

Living Building Challenge Standard 3.0 requires on-site backup energy storage, enough to power emergency lighting—defined as at least ten percent of the building's lighting load—and refrigeration for at least one week. As the first project to take on Version 3.0, Arch Nexus found itself on the "bleeding edge" with this requirement. Batteries could not contain any Red List materials, such as lead or cadmium, which left salt water batteries as the suitable choice. These are a type of "wet-cell" battery that rely on a chemical reaction between air, concentrated salt water, and a magnesium anode. Salt water batteries are non-toxic and non-flammable, and safer and easier to recycle than lithium-ion batteries. These batteries are not widely available commercially; consequently, they are very expensive. The number of batteries required not only represented a considerable cost, they would physically take up a lot of valuable real estate in the building. In addition, the code requires that if a building includes more than 50 gallons of certain hazardous materials typically associated with batteries (e.g. lead-acid or nickel-cadmium), they must be housed in a fire-rated and ventilated room. Arch Nexus had to comply with this requirement even though the salt-water batteries do not represent a fire or toxic material hazard.

Kingston appealed to the ILFI, making the case that the energy storage requirement placed an unreasonable burden on project teams and requesting that daily regeneration from on-site solar be part of the battery sizing calculation. Although the Institute did not grant his request, in the next iteration of the Living Building Challenge, Standard 3.1, the resiliency requirement has been altered. Now all projects can take advantage of grid-tied power regeneration using on-site solar.

The battery bank at Arch Nexus SAC is housed in a dedicated room that was designed during the construction phase of the project. The batteries can cycle 3000 times before their capacity is diminished to 70 percent, and will help make the Arch Nexus SAC building a beacon of resilience during the next natural disaster.

Solatubes are a critical part
of the daylighting strategy
for this one-story building.

DANGER

RISK OF FALL
KEEP OFF

PLASTIC DOMES SURFACES WILL NOT
SUPPORT BODY WEIGHT

87

"Automation will never replace human ingenuity. If you're willing to invest the time and effort to create a culture of conservation, you don't need to spend money on automation."

KENNER KINGSTON
Arch Nexus

"Building automation is great. But when people come to rely on it and they're not actively engaged in following through and checking to make sure that these things are actually working the way they are supposed to be working, sometimes really bad things can happen. If Jurassic Park taught us anything, it's that an overreliance on automation leads to dinosaurs eating people."

BRIAN CASSIL
Arch Nexus

"We've become accustomed to just using the lights like you would at home. Do you need the light on? Turn it on. Do you need it off? Turn it off."

ERICA MCBRIDE
Arch Nexus

Many of the energy-saving systems at Arch Nexus SAC are manually operated.

ENGAGED OCCUPANTS

The biggest factor in the Arch Nexus SAC building's performance is one that is often overlooked: occupant behavior.

Arch Nexus wanted to earn full certification as quickly as possible. From their experience in Salt Lake City, Kingston knew that engaged, educated occupants can greatly impact the building's energy usage, and he understood that training staff well before they moved into their new office would help them meet the certification goal in Sacramento in the shortest possible amount of time.

Arch Nexus partnered with a software company called Sustain3 to develop an occupant engagement and training platform called InHABIT. This is a social media-based platform which "gamifies" learning. Topics are broken down into three- to five-minute packets of information which start broadly but narrow in focus over time. The platform uses a "learn and earn" reward system. A user reads the information and takes a quiz to verify that they read the material. Staff earn points for themselves and their team for each module they complete, and the friendly competition encourages participation. Nearly a year before moving into the building, Arch Nexus began deploying training modules to their Sacramento staff.

Kingston has found that people are more likely to implement strategies at work if they try them at home first. Consequently, the third step of InHABIT is a "call to action." For example, if the unit explains how the electricity grid works, the user is prompted to go home and examine their power bill, implement energy-saving measures, and compare usage over time. Staff are also encouraged to share their results and ideas about saving energy in a community forum.

Arch Nexus did not have the budget for a complex building automation system. Even if they did, they did not want to undermine the important role of occupants. Having engaged occupants also lessens the reliance on building automation; for example, even though the building includes simple automation features such as occupancy sensors, staff prefer to turn lights on and off themselves.

THE HEALTH & HAPPINESS PETAL

The Benefits of a Biophilic Building

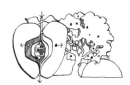

ACTIVATE ENGAGE

INHABIT

91

The Health & Happiness Petal: **THE BENEFITS OF A BIOPHILIC BUILDING**

THE HEALTH + HAPPINESS PETAL
LIVING BUILDING CHALLENGE VERSION 3.0

PETAL INTENT

The intent of the Health and Happiness Petal is to focus on the most important environmental conditions that must be present to create robust, healthy spaces, rather than to address all of the potential ways that an interior environment could be compromised. Many developments provide substandard conditions for health and productivity and human potential is greatly diminished in these places. By focusing attention on the major pathways of health we create environments designed to optimize our well-being.

PETAL IMPERATIVES

- Civilized Environment
- Healthy Interior Environment
- Biophilic Environment

92

An enclosed office that was part of the original interior plan has been transformed into an architectural library which all staff can access.

The intent of the Health and Happiness Petal is "to focus on the most important environmental conditions that must be present to create robust, healthy spaces."

For Arch Nexus, this goal was especially pertinent, as they were seeking to create a healthy, stimulating workplace for their own employees. The tenant space that they were renting in Sacramento fell far short of this ideal. The office was located next to a busy interstate highway. Even if there had been much to look at, forty-eight inch dividers between each workstation blocked the views out the windows. Staff could not open the fixed windows; indoor air quality was poor and daylighting minimal. This was in stark contrast to the Salt Lake City office, where daylighting had been used to such great effect.

These unpleasant conditions increased the sense of urgency around the regeneration project. At the very least, Arch Nexus hoped to extricate staff from the tenant space and relocate them to a more appealing workplace—one that was on par with the Salt Lake City office. But they had more ambitious goals; namely, to create a place which brought out the best in all occupants, and which encouraged them to thrive personally and professionally.

The firm sought to achieve this in every phase of the project. During design, their efforts focused on creating a biophilic environment that is illuminated with natural light and which fosters connections between people, nature, and place. During construction, the team strove to avoid introducing harmful contaminants into the space. And in the occupancy phase, they sought to educate staff on what it means to occupy a Living Building—a process that continues to this day.

93

The Health & Happiness Petal: **THE BENEFITS OF A BIOPHILIC BUILDING**

LESSONS FROM SALT LAKE CITY

Imperative 07: Civilized Environment states that every regularly occupied space must have operable windows that provide access to fresh air and daylight.

An open design is one of the best strategies to ensure all occupants in an office environment have access to views, fresh air, and daylight. Arch Nexus had implemented an open plan at their first Salt Lake City office, but it went beyond simply nixing cubicles and minimizing enclosed offices. In 2003, Arch Nexus became a hundred-person firm. During the design of the company's first office space, they were faced with organizing one hundred workstations into an appealing workplace. Leadership had identified that employees work best together in groups of colleagues, or "tribes," so they decided to divide the office space into smaller, more humane quadrants of about twenty-five workstations each. Borrowing the metaphor of a city, they used the terms "boulevard," "street," and "neighborhood" to describe the quadrants, and even named the neighborhoods based on their geographic orientation. The concept stuck, and to this day, the fundamental operating unit of the company is called a Neighborhood.

Years later, when Arch Nexus was renovating the building that would become Arch Nexus SLC, they planned the interior so that all employees would have access to the centrally located daylight courtyard. In a later phase of this renovation, Arch Nexus added a lobby and second story. They initially thought this second-story space would function as "overflow," rather than dedicated office space, as they did not want staff to feel isolated from the rest of their colleagues. They also wanted it to have the same daylighting benefits as the main office, even though it did not have access to the courtyard. Brian Cassil ran some daylighting simulations and designed in several tubular skylights from Solatube. These units concentrate light and enable daylighting even in spaces with high, open ceilings. The daylighting rendered the second-story space so inviting and pleasant that it was named "The Loft" and incorporated as a fifth Neighborhood.

BRINGING THE OUTSIDE IN

The design team intended to import the Neighborhood concept to the Arch Nexus SAC renovation and illuminate the space with both top and side lighting; however, they had to work with the constraints of the existing building and site.

> "Our staff loves operating the windows. It's very pleasurable, the sense of control and connection to the city. People were originally concerned about the noise from the street, but it turns out it's actually quite nice. It makes you feel not segregated. There's a diurnal cycle to it; an ebb and a flow. You're part of the life of the city."
>
> **KENNER KINGSTON**
> Arch Nexus

A central daylit courtyard was not an option, and the existing building's orientation limited daylighting from the south. While the one-story floorplan enabled daylighting from above, the row of deciduous trees on 10th Street shaded a good portion of the roof.

To maximize access to views and fresh air, the work stations are located on the east and south sides of the floorplan, while common areas are arrayed along the west wall. The open plan ensures all have access to views, not only of the outdoors, but of the Living Wall on the opposite side. Because of its corner location and access to even daylighting, the north side is dedicated to the entry, lobby, and meeting areas.

As in Salt Lake City, Neighborhoods at Arch Nexus SAC—called Valley and River—are named for their geographic orientation. In the original design, three enclosed offices, designated for the Sacramento office's three senior principals, separated the Neighborhoods. These offices were placed in the center of the space to preserve the views for the rest of the staff.

95

Some of the existing paving was converted into an outdoor retreat space for staff.

Solatubes bring light in from above, so that even workstations away from the windows benefit from daylighting. Operable tilt-and-turn windows allow employees to control access to fresh air. A signal light lets everyone know when conditions are favorable for natural ventilation, at which time the HVAC system is shut off manually.

One of the issues that consistently arises with open office plans is occupants' dissatisfaction with noise levels. Arch Nexus dealt with this issue by imposing some common courtesy measures: staff use headphones when engaged in conference calls and reserve loud conversations for the offices or the Design Lab. The design also helps mitigate noise. Exposed wood beams help absorb sound, as does the carpeting under the workstations.

Outdoor gathering spaces at the front and rear of the building encourage staff to take advantage of Sacramento's generous shoulder seasons and spend part of their workday outdoors. In addition to the public art sculpture at the building's public entry on R Street, part of the original parking area has been converted to a "picnic patio" on the building's south side, just off the kitchen. This space was conceived and deliberately created to contribute to the health and happiness of Arch Nexus employees. Here staff can work, hold a meeting, or take a break at the custom-built table and benches. This semi-private space is enhanced with food-bearing plants, shaded by the solar PV canopy, and sheltered from the street by the rainwater cisterns.

"We are going to be forever changed; we're never going to think about a project in the same way again. Site is artificial. It doesn't exist. Property lines are not real. But place is, as the LBC says, real, alive, and whole. And when you really get into that concept it's about place, which is bigger than the property: it's the community; it's the neighborhood; it's the block—it's this whole set of interconnections."

KENNER KINGSTON
Arch Nexus

REGENERATIVE RETROFIT: *California's First Living Building*

IMPERATIVE 08: HEALTHY INTERIOR ENVIRONMENT

Imperative 08: Healthy Interior Environment outlines several requirements that together work to ensure good indoor air quality for building occupants.

These measures include a prohibition on smoking, dedicated exhaust systems for certain areas such as kitchen and bathrooms, and strategies that reduce tracking of particulate matter into the building. This Imperative also requires indoor air quality testing before occupancy and nine months afterwards.

Arch Nexus and MarketOne complied with all of these measures. Team members maintained constant vigilance to ensure materials that could possibly off-gas harmful chemicals never entered the job site or the completed building. After occupancy, staff adopted a cleaning protocol which Arch Nexus had initially developed for their Salt Lake City office.

One of the most impactful decisions Arch Nexus made was to reconfigure workstations from a previous office, rather than purchase new office furniture. Unfortunately, the upholstery and finishes in new furniture often contain harmful chemicals such as flame retardants and VOCs; consequently, these products often become a significant path for contaminants through off-gassing. Modifying and reusing furniture from a previous office also helped with Red List vetting and conserved materials and costs.

The building easily passed the initial air quality test, prior to occupancy. However, when the second test took place nine months later, in November of 2017, the building did not meet the threshold for fine particulate matter or VOCs.

The team immediately set out to find the sources of these pollutants.

Initially, they did not think that the source of pollution could have originated from outside of the building. They knew that in general, air quality inside of buildings is worse than outside and that most indoor air pollutants come from within the building itself. In addition, the remodeled envelope was well sealed and insulated, and the fan-coil units were fitted with MERV 13 filters.

Instead, they examined all possible sources of contamination, and even considered the possibility that product samples requested by clients—samples which had not been vetted for Red List chemicals—could be contaminating the space. Building Manager Erica McBride suggested removing the samples from the building, and even stored some in the trunk of her car.

Arch Nexus rented air scrubbers and borrowed air purifiers and commissioned a second test, but fine particulate matter was still five times over the acceptable limit. Finally, they began looking at outdoor air as the potential source of this dust.

The Arch Nexus site is subject to air pollution from a number of local and regional sources. Air often settles in and around the Sacramento River, which is just a few miles from the building. Construction is a daily reality in the up-and-coming neighborhood; at the time of

> "When you walk into this building, the first thing you see is glass and plants. You feel like it's more inviting to come into this building versus an artificially lit, down on the bottom floor of the basement-type building."
>
> **JEFF DAVIS**
> Arch Nexus

> "The bright light on the wall is the natural ventilation sensor. When the outside temperature and humidity are appropriate, it turns on to say, you're okay to open the windows if you want to. What it doesn't tell you is if the air quality is appropriate."
>
> **KENNER KINGSTON**
> Arch Nexus

> "Everything's great when the windows are open. But you're bringing in a lot of PM 2.5 and PM 10 in. Sacramento air quality is not great."
>
> **KENNER KINGSTON**
> Arch Nexus

> "We were checking particulates because that was the one area we kept failing. We wanted to flush out the building, but Patty said, we're going to let all this formaldehyde from the fires inside and people should not be breathing that, air tests or not. She said close the windows and we're not opening them until this is gone."
>
> **KENNER KINGSTON**
> Arch Nexus

97

Staff at Arch Nexus SAC have learned to check local outdoor air quality before opening windows.

the second air quality test, a market across the street was being remodeled.

In addition, Northern California was on fire. Over a dozen wildfires had ignited in October of 2017, including the devastating Tubbs fire, which swept through Napa, Sonoma, and Lake Counties and destroyed entire neighborhoods in the city of Santa Rosa. By November, fires were burning in eight northern counties, and smoke from these wildfires was impacting regions far beyond their sources.

McBride suggested purchasing a residential monitoring product called a Foobot, so that they could continuously monitor

air quality inside the office. This device connects to Wi-Fi and provides real-time data on several metrics, including temperature, humidity, VOCs, and particulate matter. McBride noticed a trend: air quality consistently dipped when staff was using natural ventilation—i.e., opening the windows.

Along with using Foobot to track indoor air quality, staff began consulting a state-sponsored site called Spare the Air to help them decide whether to open windows or not. At the suggestion of the Commissioning Agent, Capital Engineering, McBride also adjusted exhaust fans to alleviate negative pressure that was sucking outside air into the building. Finally, in March 2018, the building passed the air quality test.

"One of the things that I love about this building is coming back to it over and over again and just watching it change. It really is a Living Building. The plants that are growing on the outside change over time. When you watch the corten metal, it was silver and then it gets a little bit red and a little bit more red. Now it's completely weathered. The building has changed and it will continue to change. The people who occupy the building will continue to evolve, too. It changes behaviors. The beauty of living in a Living Building is you're meant to change with it."

JEFF DAVIS
Arch Nexus

A BIOPHILIC FRAMEWORK

Imperative 09: Biophilic Environment states that every project must be designed to include elements that nurture the innate human/nature connection. Project teams must engage in a one-day exploration on the "biophilic design potential" of their project and must develop a biophilic framework which incorporates aspects of all six of the biophilic elements, or categories, as defined by Stephen Kellert.

These biophilic attributes range from the simple incorporation of features from the natural environment such as water, air, color, sunlight, and plants to more complex concepts such as "Spirit of Place" and "Age, Change, and the Patina of Time."

Many features in the building embrace more than one aspect of biophilic design; in this way, their layered functions mimic an ecosystem, where plants, animals, and microorganisms integrate into a functional and beautiful whole.

Biophilic design helps create an environment that is simultaneously soothing and stimulating. Many studies have quantified the benefits of biophilic design to building occupants. Daylighting and views of nature have positive impacts on worker productivity, well-being, and health; the presence of natural light can even boost sales in retail environments!

Because Arch Nexus occupies the building they designed, they are able to experience the benefits of biophilic design for themselves. Employees report that they enjoy the connections with the outside and street life. They enjoy the freedom of controlling windows, watching the plants grow, and witnessing the building change over time. They have also learned to connect their actions and behavior to the building's performance. It's a dynamic relationship that is continuously evolving, as people learn and grow along with the building they occupy.

ENVIRONMENTAL FEATURES

LIGHT + SPACE

NATURAL SHAPES
+ FORMS

EVOLVED
HUMAN-NATURE
RELATIONSHIPS

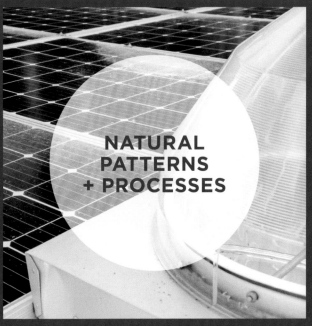

NATURAL
PATTERNS
+ PROCESSES

PLACE-BASED
RELATIONSHIPS

The Health & Happiness Petal: **THE BENEFITS OF A BIOPHILIC BUILDING**

> "There is such a wide variety of biophilic pieces on any project that it's not hard to find ones that are really applicable to your project. In fact, some of the difficulty can be getting down to what are the most important or the simplest ones that can really have an impact. I've found that if you're trying to incorporate everything into your design it gets a little bit diluted. So it's really important to find those intersections where different ideas meet."

JEFF DAVIS
Arch Nexus

102

THE LIVING WALL: A BIOPHILIC EXPERIENCE

Perhaps no other feature illustrates the layered functionality and interconnectedness made possible through biophilic design than the interior Living Wall.

This curving wall of live plants is certainly one of the most visible of the building's biophilic features, and it was designed so that as many people as possible would enjoy its benefits. It is not only the first thing you see as you enter the lobby, it is also visible from any of the workstations. Staff pass by the Living Wall on the way to the kitchen, locker room, and bathrooms; it is also deliberately visible from outside of the building and serves as a transitional element, linking inside with outside, and the lobby to the offices and conference room.

The Living Wall is a visual reminder of the hydrologic cycle and the role human occupants play in it. Rainwater is captured in the cisterns, used by building occupants, and cycles through the roots and leaves of the plants. The actions of Arch Nexus staff impact both the quantity and quality of the greywater that is ultimately used and filtered by the plants, which through the natural process of respiration evaporate excess greywater and help filter indoor air.

The plants engage the senses and arouse the imagination, introducing natural shapes—the leaves and growth forms of the plants and the curve of the wall itself—into a rectilinear space. The plants offer a stimulating contrast of shades, textures, and shapes, and the vibrant green hues provide a pleasing contrast to the weathered metal of the front desk. Finally, the Living Wall recalls the cycles of growth and the nature of change, as plants grow, thrive, and even eventually die.

103

REEDS AND RAILS: THE INTERSECTION OF NATURE AND PLACE

During their initial exploration into place, Jeff Davis, Charlie Downs, Joe Yee, and Kenner Kingston learned that native grasses were a key component of the region's ecosystem. The more they learned, the more subtleties they discovered.

For instance, they learned that grasses growing in the floodplain would be tamped down by floodwaters, but would rebound once the water receded. Similarly, the movements of indigenous people tracked the ebbing and flowing of the waters.

Davis was intrigued by the practical ways in which the region's first inhabitants used native plants, but also how these plants influenced the aesthetic aspects of their culture. For example, grasses woven into clothing and ceremonial headdresses created strong and rigid vertical patterns, whereas a bank of marsh tule lining a wetland created a more organic but equally compelling rhythm of its own.

Davis felt like he was onto something. He began exploring the site's more recent history. The building site sits on an old railroad corridor which developed into a warehouse district where trains would come through and unload their goods. Davis and his team noted the pattern of railroad ties, the rhythm of the rails, and the rectilinear lines of the warehouse buildings. They began looking at how to replicate these strong and complementary rhythms of the reeds and rails—natural and manmade; organic and formal—into the building itself.

The "reeds and rails" theme found its strongest expression in the arrangement of metal panels on the building exterior. Davis varied the width and hues of these panels to create a subtle rhythm. The mostly white panels appear uniform at certain times of the day, but in more angled light the contrasting shades and finishes become more apparent. Overlain on this manmade palette is the organic pattern of leaves cast by the row of London planetrees to the east.

Learning more about the seasonal ebb and flow of the floodwaters and how these movements shaped the marsh plants spurred Davis and his team to think about water as structure: for example, the way water holds a lily pad on the surface of the water, giving it its distinctive shape. This concept inspired Davis to add a dark-colored recessed metal panel all along the bottom of the building. Metaphorically, this dark strip represents the floodwaters and provides a connection to a cyclical ecological event that occurred there for centuries.

All of these elements work together to create a rich intersection of nature and place that is more felt than observed.

> "The manmade use of nature, the rhythms in the rails and the rhythms in those headdresses, becomes very straight and rigid. But then we were able to juxtapose that against real nature, and let real nature have an impact on the building. When the leaves are on the trees, it creates this incredible dappled light that becomes part of the façade of the building."
>
> **JEFF DAVIS**
> Arch Nexus

> "It was an 'Aha' moment for us. All the study we'd been doing on place and all of the study we'd be doing about nature and the indigenous people intersected. We realized that these rhythms are something special that connect all of these things together."
>
> **JEFF DAVIS**
> Arch Nexus

> "It's not readily understood that the exterior panels with their different colors were created from understanding the indigenous plants and other stuff that was originally here before. No one looks at the building and goes, 'Oh, hey, indigenous plants.'"
>
> **JEFF DAVIS**
> Arch Nexus

The Health & Happiness Petal: **THE BENEFITS OF A BIOPHILIC BUILDING**

MAKING CONNECTIONS

The team's early biophilic studies led Davis to think about how the design could foster connections to history, place, and the community. The entry sequence is a direct manifestation of this intention, and like the Living Wall, it serves many biophilic functions.

Because they were working with an existing building, they could not change its orientation, which is aligned with Sacramento's street grid. However, Davis decided to design an entry sequence

which honored the earth's grid and aligns with true north, creating a geographic connection to place. The angled entry would also serve as a daily reminder to the design professionals as they entered the building of the importance of building orientation and its influence on daylighting, solar gain, and energy use. Finally, rotating the entry oriented part of the building toward the Historic R Street archway, sending a strong message of welcome and inviting people to learn about the creative work happening inside.

The image of grasses bent over with the weight of their own seeds influenced the design, as did the bending of the rivers near their confluence. Davis and his team kept these curving motions in mind when thinking about how people would enter and flow through the building, and drew on them to introduce curves into an otherwise rectilinear space.

A BIOPHILIC PROCESS

It all started with a biophilic study of the curves of the grasses and also looking at the curves of the rivers at the confluence. As we studied these, we really started to think about connections. That's where this front entry piece really started to evolve. We wanted to be connected to the community.

As we started to explore how to open the building up to the community, we realized another important piece that ties back to nature—and one that is really important to us as designers—is the orientation of the building. It's always important to know which way is north; it's one of the first things we're taught.

We had an existing building; we didn't get to choose the orientation. But what we did do was rotate the entry sequence back on true north—both to connect us back to nature and to remind us as designers that orientation is a fundamental that we always need to remember. And it connected us back to the community.

In nature, sometimes you're walking along a trail and as it goes through really thick trees, you really can't see anything. Then all of a sudden the trail bends and the trees stop and there's this huge meadow in front of you. It creates an awe-inspiring experience because there was this compression around you and then a release. That's a biophilic human experience.

We have this compressed area at the entry that then opens up to this great space with the green wall, and then it compresses again as you go back into the office area. We're trying to create biophilic experiences for the occupants and the community. It elevates their motivation, which elevates their productivity.

JEFF DAVIS
Arch Nexus

The entry sequence into the building, through the lobby, and into the main office area was designed to be an inspiring biophilic experience. Savannah creatures that we are, or once were, most people feel an intuitive sense of release upon leaving a more confined area for a more spacious one.

Davis likens the experience of entering the building to walking through a thick grove of trees which opens up into a meadow. Space in the entry is constricted, expands in the lobby, and constricts again as you pass by the Living Wall, finally opening up into the main office.

THE MATERIALS PETAL

Conservation at the Core

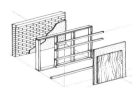

The exterior metal panels are one of many
Declare-labeled products used in the building.

109

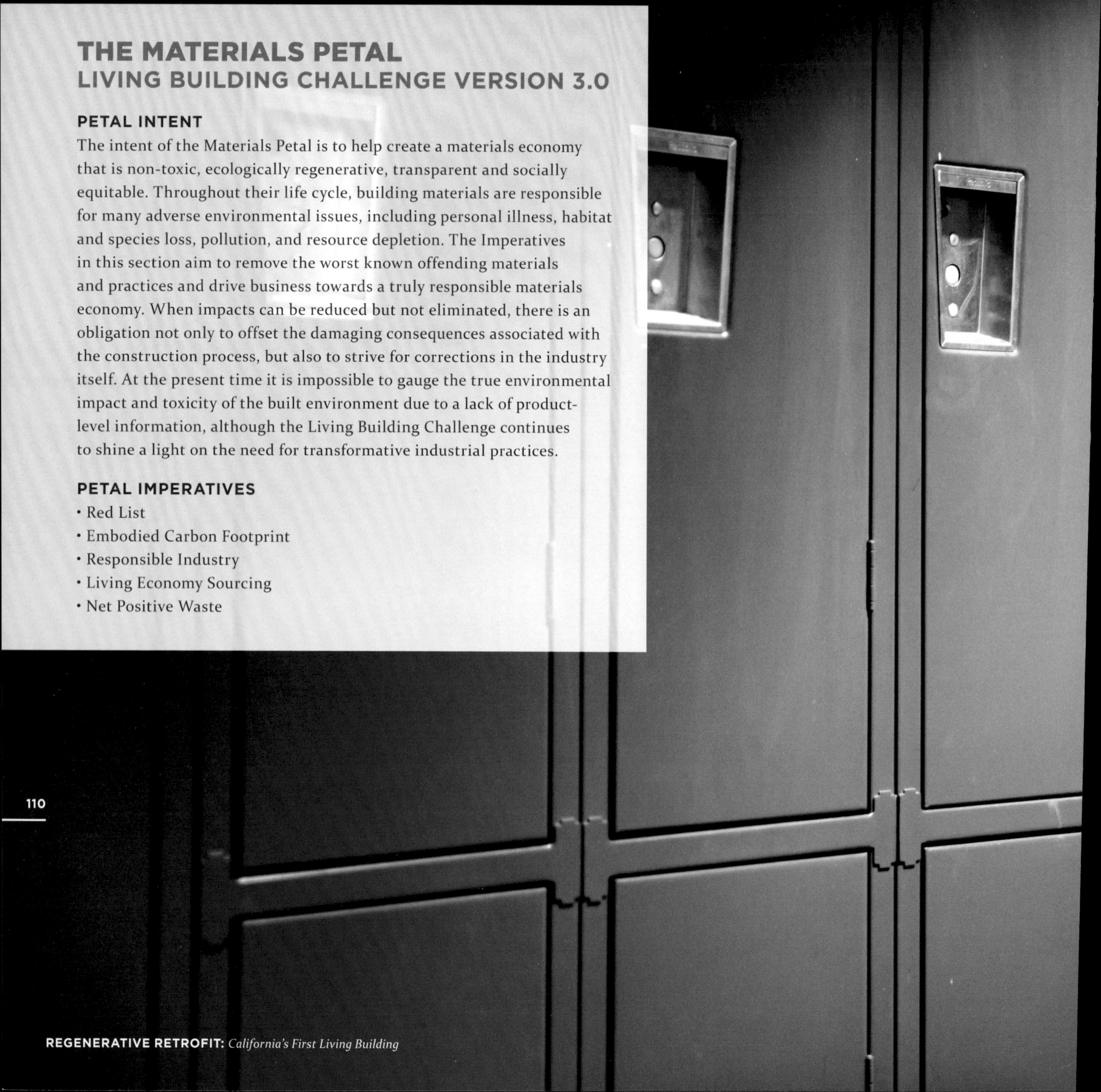

THE MATERIALS PETAL
LIVING BUILDING CHALLENGE VERSION 3.0

PETAL INTENT

The intent of the Materials Petal is to help create a materials economy that is non-toxic, ecologically regenerative, transparent and socially equitable. Throughout their life cycle, building materials are responsible for many adverse environmental issues, including personal illness, habitat and species loss, pollution, and resource depletion. The Imperatives in this section aim to remove the worst known offending materials and practices and drive business towards a truly responsible materials economy. When impacts can be reduced but not eliminated, there is an obligation not only to offset the damaging consequences associated with the construction process, but also to strive for corrections in the industry itself. At the present time it is impossible to gauge the true environmental impact and toxicity of the built environment due to a lack of product-level information, although the Living Building Challenge continues to shine a light on the need for transformative industrial practices.

PETAL IMPERATIVES

- Red List
- Embodied Carbon Footprint
- Responsible Industry
- Living Economy Sourcing
- Net Positive Waste

"It made us think about using things because they're necessary, not just aesthetically beautiful. You're not just putting things there for the sake of putting them there."

JEFF DAVIS
Arch Nexus

Modern buildings are carbon and resource intensive. Their construction requires large amounts of materials that are often produced through energy-intensive processes and transported over long distances. Buildings are often built quickly and cheaply, and too often the negative impacts are externalized, usually to poorer communities. Too many building materials contain toxic ingredients that cause harm to those involved in their manufacture, to construction laborers and to the building occupants.

111

The five Imperatives under the Materials Petal seek to transform construction, so that buildings are designed and built for the long term, without toxins or harmful extractive processes, and where nothing is ever wasted.

Originally installed when Arch Nexus SLC was still a fitness center, these lockers are in their third incarnation at Arch Nexus SAC.

The Materials Petal: **CONSERVATION AT THE CORE**

Pole steps, sourced from decommissioned power poles, serve as structural elements for the exterior trellis.

"When you walk through our project and you look up into the roof and see what was here before, I think that this is really beautiful. And it wouldn't be beautiful if we had just dropped in a ceiling and covered all that up.

ROBB HARROP
Arch Nexus

"Existing buildings are the built environment; we need to adapt, reuse, and regenerate them appropriately so they can continue to be part of our future."

HOLLI ADAMS
Arch Nexus

First and foremost, and unlike any other Living Building to date, Arch Nexus prioritized a project that was an adaptive reuse of an existing building, which by its nature dramatically lowers a project's carbon footprint and material use. The team's approach was to maximize the value of already spent resources through regenerative design principles.

Conservation is at the heart of this project: conservation of open space and municipal infrastructure; conservation of the materials in the existing building; and conservation of new materials through salvage, reuse, and avoidance. Thoughtful operations conserve materials while the building is occupied, and finally, practices that promote deconstruction at the end of the building's life will conserve materials in the future.

When it came to specific materials, the design team's overall strategy was two-fold: use as many Declare-labeled products as they could, and incorporate salvaged materials whenever possible.

The team prioritized materials with lower relative carbon intensity. Salvaged materials were preferred over new wood lumber; wood over steel; and steel over concrete.

The project reduces the volume of materials by leveraging the existing structure whenever possible. For example, the primary floor finish is sealed concrete rather than carpeting, and the open design reveals the ceiling structure. In places, the concrete is stained, hinting at its previous incarnation as a print shop, and some of the original perimeter columns were left in place. These choices not only saved materials, but preserved some of the history and character of the original building.

Finally, every design decision and material choice was governed by the overall vision of how the project would connect to place. Every material and element had to have purpose, and even aesthetic value was measured by how successfully it helped connect the project to culture, history, geography, and the natural environment.

112

A DAUNTING TASK

Imperative 10: Red List prohibits the inclusion of any material containing any one of twenty-two chemical categories.

The Red List includes some chemicals commonly used in building products, such as polyvinyl chloride (PVC) and halogenated flame retardants; consequently, achieving this Imperative has proven one of the most challenging for project teams.

Patty Karapinar of Arch Nexus acted as Construction Administrator on the project and led the process of vetting products for the Red List. She drew from a deep background in sustainability and LEED project experience; even so, the process of vetting materials came with a steep learning curve. She knew she needed to get started well before construction began, and she quickly connected with other project teams. In addition to receiving valuable advice, she acquired examples of tracking sheets and questionnaire forms that other teams had developed. She also found the Dialogue especially helpful. Hosted by the ILFI, the Dialogue is an online platform that allows team members from registered projects to post questions and view answers from ILFI's technical experts. Registered members can also pore through archived conversations.

As construction progressed, Karapinar worked closely with Sean Kotke and Kenny Dees of MarketOne on materials vetting. As Project Manager, Dees estimated the job and ran it through operations, while Kotke, as Project Superintendent, oversaw the day-to-day management of the project.

The team of Karapinar, Dees, and Kotke tried to "pre-vet" as many materials as possible; however, once construction commenced they found themselves having to vet materials as quickly as possible to stay on schedule. At times Karapinar would ask for three versions of the same product so that she could research them simultaneously, with the hope that at least one of them would be compliant. At other times Kotke had to halt one aspect of construction to wait for a material to be cleared. They "tag-teamed": Karapinar would take documentation obtained through the submittal process and fill in the gaps, or Dees would contact a supplier to obtain missing information from Karapinar's files.

As owner's rep, Kingston wanted to adhere to the schedule so that Arch Nexus staff could move into the remodeled office by the end of 2016. However, he did not want the contractor or any of his employees to bear the burden should they discover a Red List item had been installed in the building. Kingston devised a system: if a product had not been completely vetted but Karapinar felt reasonably sure that it was compliant, she was to bring the information to Kingston. He would then issue the final judgment on whether or not to install it; meanwhile, Karapinar would continue the vetting process. In only one case did an item, a plumbing part, have to be removed and replaced, at very little cost.

The Materials Petal: **CONSERVATION AT THE CORE**

LIVING BUILDING
CHALLENGE 3.0
REGISTERED PROJECT

ARCH | NEXUS SAC

*"At the front and back
of the job site there was
a sign that said, 'You're
entering a Living Building
Challenge project. Do
not enter if you haven't
received the training; do
not use combustion-based
equipment.' Live the values
of the project. And you
had to go past that sign
every day as you came in
and out."*

KENNER KINGSTON
Arch Nexus

EVERYONE ON BOARD

**Early on, before the builder had been
officially selected, Arch Nexus invited
MarketOne and their major subcontractors
to attend a presentation on the Living
Building Challenge—in part to gauge their
response, but also to let them know what
they were getting themselves into.**

At that initial meeting, Kingston proposed that, for the duration
of the project, no one could enter the jobsite until they had had
the Living Building Challenge training. Everyone agreed.

Once MarketOne was officially hired, Arch Nexus and
MarketOne collaborated on signage for the job site, which
announced to people that they were entering a Living Building
Challenge project and reminded them that they needed to have
attended a training session before stepping foot on the site.

Dees and Kotke understood the importance of maintaining
vigilance as construction progressed. Unintentionally allowing
a prohibited product or material on the site could have dire

consequences. They decided to err on the side of caution: if a
product or material was not explicitly vetted and approved,
it could not come onto the job site, even if the item was not a
building material. In several cases this became highly nuanced;
for example, someone might obtain a product that was the
correct brand name but a slightly different version of the
approved product. For this reason, it was crucial that Kotke
stay current on the paperwork on vetted products provided by
Karapinar and Dees.

The vigilance extended to manufacturers; for example,
MarketOne requested a concrete mix that contained simply
water, cement, sand, and rocks, with no other additives. Dees
remained in contact with the plant manager to ensure that
their concrete was mixed correctly. At other times, the team
worked closely with manufacturers who were willing to tweak
formulations or make substitutions so that the product complied
with the Red List. For example, window manufacturer Jeld-Wen
swapped out some PVC components so that their windows would
comply with the Red List. Although this was a custom order for
Arch Nexus, the company learned they could provide Red List
free alternatives to other customers, too.

RESPONSIBLE INDUSTRY AND LIVING ECONOMY SOURCING

Imperative 12: Responsible Industry states that all wood used in a project must either be certified to the 100% labeling standards set by the Forest Stewardship Council (FSC) or be salvaged or harvested from the site. It also sets a minimum threshold for the number of Declare-labeled products a project must include.

The team incorporated a large amount of salvaged wood, much of it recovered from the original building. Studs were reused, and other lumber was repurposed as backing or blocking. The casework fabricator also laminated studs into benches for the locker room.

The project team benefited from the site's proximity to the Pacific Northwest. New lumber came from FSC-certified forests located in Washington, Oregon, and Northern California; however, the team discovered that the certification documents did not identify the particular forest. Karapinar needed this information to satisfy Imperative 13: Living Economy Sourcing. This Imperative sets thresholds for the percentage of construction materials that must be sourced within a certain distance from the building site. Because she could only pinpoint the region, not the exact location, Karapinar decided to pick the spot within the region that was farthest from the project site.

Although the project used local and regional materials and salvaged items as much as possible, the team still found the Living Economy Sourcing Imperative difficult to achieve, in large part because it uses the materials construction budget as its gauge. In other words, expensive items such as solar photovoltaic modules take up a proportionately larger portion of the budget than lower-cost items.

Fortunately, the team was able to source solar modules from SolarWorld, a manufacturer located in Oregon. Other high-dollar materials such as the metal panels were manufactured in California. Still, there were several key products that the team could not source locally, most notably the mechanical system and the Jets vacuum flush toilets, which came from South Korea and Norway, respectively. Together these items consumed the entire budget for materials sourced from more than 5,000 km away from the project site.

5000 km
24%

2500 km
CONSULTANTS

1000 km
25%

500 km
30%

The materials and services for Arch Nexus SAC have been sourced as close as possible to Sacramento. This preference for place-based solutions stimulates local economic growth, strengthens community ties and minimizes environmental impacts associated with the transportation of products and people.

MATERIAL SOURCE

MOVING THE NEEDLE

Since the launch of the Declare program, in 2012, the task of materials vetting has become slightly less onerous. Declare is a transparency program which encourages manufacturers to disclose every "ingredient" in their products, and to replace harmful ingredients with benign alternatives.

Declare offers three types of labels: Red List Free, LBC Compliant, and Declared. The hope is that project teams who are seeking to minimize the negative health impacts of their projects will prefer products which have been "pre-vetted" through Declare, thus spurring the materials economy toward greater transparency and health.

The Arch Nexus SAC regeneration includes thirty-five Declare-labeled products, well above the minimum requirement of one Declare product per 500 m² of gross building area. The range of Declare-labeled projects in the building—from weather barrier, sealants, and paints, to drywall, insulation, and carpet tiles—is welcome proof that manufacturers are embracing the program. Early adopters in certain industry sectors—paints and insulation, for example—are making the process of sourcing these categories of products much easier. For example, Karapinar was able to source Declare-labeled paints, primer, stain, varnish, and concrete sealer from Benjamin Moore and Imperial Paints.

Karapinar and her team also helped spur at least two manufacturers to pursue or expedite their own Declare labels.

They sourced a curtain wall system from Kawneer, which already had an associated Declare label, but the building also required a storefront section with operable windows. Kawneer had been planning to seek a Declare label for this system but had not yet started the application. The process of material vetting required the manufacturer to provide detailed product information, including an inventory of all product ingredients and the percentages of each—the same information they would need to qualify for a Declare label. The process spurred Kawneer to acquire Declare label for this system more quickly. Today the company has many Declare-labeled products and has also created a complete manufacturer's material ingredient inventory known as the Material Transparency Summary (MTS), a tool which helps people understand and evaluate the health impacts of products.

The Red List criteria also apply to new systems, furniture and other interior products that are affixed to the structure. One of the last items to be sourced and installed was the glass markerboards for the conference room and design lab. Arch Nexus worked with Clarus, a company which manufactures white boards and dry erase boards, to source them. The company was not familiar with the Red List, but once Karapinar introduced them to the Living Building Challenge they were enthusiastic about working with her to provide glassboards which were Red List free. Shortly thereafter, Clarus obtained Declare Labels for three of their products, and as of this writing the company holds five.

"We thought, how are we ever going to do this? We don't want to use a general Red List exception every time we come up with a problem; that's not the point. You could do that, but it's not authentic and it's kind of lazy."

PATTY KARAPINAR
Arch Nexus

MATERIAL CHALLENGES

For Karapinar, Dees, and Kotke, the process of vetting materials was both eye opening and disturbing. They were surprised to discover that many building materials contain Red List substances, and that some manufacturers are unaware of the potentially harmful chemicals contained within their products.

Some of the most difficult items to vet were coatings and adhesives, plumbing parts, structural components, and products made with multiple components, which manufacturers often sourced from other manufacturers. Some were not used to being asked such detailed questions about their products, and at times would not or could not provide clear answers. For example, metal hangers, which support loads and reinforce connections in the building structure, are often galvanized with a protective coating of zinc. Some galvanized coatings contain lead, a Red List item, while others do not. When Karapinar questioned manufacturers about their coatings, some would tell her what they thought she wanted to hear but balked when she asked them to put their claim in writing. In other cases, manufacturers did not want to release the proprietary ingredients contained in their products; this was especially true for certain categories of products, such as epoxies.

The team even ran into Red List challenges with repurposed items. For example, Arch Nexus wanted to reuse some workstation furniture from a previous office, and they shipped the pieces to Los Angeles so they could be physically modified. There they discovered that the wiring system would also have to be removed. Not only was the wiring insulated with PVC, a Red List item, it was not compliant with California's Title 24 building code.

At times, salvaging became a solution when the team could not vet new materials. For example, Karapinar could not source certain plumbing parts that complied with the Red List, in part because the Red List Imperative added Chromium 6 to the Red List in Living Building Challenge 3.0. Most chrome-finished plumbing parts and fixtures utilize chromium 6 because of its durability; however, this form of chromium is a known carcinogen. Karapinar did not want to give up and apply for a Red List exception—an allowable path that recognizes that a transparent and toxin-free materials economy is a work in progress. MarketOne's plumbing subcontractor was working on another renovation project elsewhere in Sacramento, so they decided to salvage the plumbing parts out of the building and use them at Arch Nexus SAC. Even though these salvaged parts also contained chromium, the ILFI ultimately approved their use because the team was not able to find Red List free alternatives.

"It's insane how many toxic materials there are in building products. Even the manufacturers themselves aren't aware of it until you start asking them questions."

PATTY KARAPINAR
Arch Nexus

"We found through the Arch Nexus project that there are little things we can do to make a difference. It opened our eyes to what's possible. Sean learned so much about purchasing and material sourcing, and Kenny now has this strong depth of knowledge on materials and Red Listing and Declare labeling. Living Buildings may not be catching on like wildfire, but LEED when it first started wasn't like wildfire either.

JAMES FITZGERALD
MarketOne

THE BLEEDING EDGE

For the Arch Nexus Sac team, one particular material best illustrates the headaches and triumphs of life on the "bleeding edge" of a pioneering regeneration project.

The exterior design of the building hinged on the pattern of vertically oriented metal panels arranged above a dark strip, representing the floodplain, which runs the length of the building. These panels were to be four different but complementary colors. Arch Nexus and MarketOne worked

with Metal Sales Manufacturing to obtain these. This company had also provided metal panels to the Bullitt Center and had demonstrated enthusiasm for the Living Building Challenge.

In addition to the aesthetic requirements, the panels needed to be protected with a durable coating which could stand up to the elements for decades. However, the industry standard for this type of coating contains hexavalent chromium and phthalates, both Red List chemicals.

At that time, Metal Sales Manufacturing was working with ValSpar to source an alternative to these coatings. ValSpar had developed a product called Fluoropon Pure that was Red List free. Metal Sales was experimenting with the coating but was not yet using it in production runs. Karapinar discussed the possibility of doing a special run with Fluropon Pure at their Los Angeles facility, even though their plant in Woodland was much closer to Sacramento. Metal Sales was willing, but they set a minimum order of panels for each color that was far in excess of what was needed.

The design team slightly altered the exterior design to include three instead of four colors of metal panels, and Metal Sales promised to produce panels using Fluropon Pure for the Arch Nexus project. But their production schedule was a moving target, and the panels were not delivered until December. MarketOne accommodated the delay by changing the detailing of other elements, such as window flashing.

Arch Nexus still had to order more panels than they needed. They were able to use some of the material as interior framing, and Metal Sales held some of the excess. Once they were able to sell the panels, they credited Arch Nexus for them.

Today Metal Sales Manufacturing holds a Declare label for metal panels coated with Fluoropon Pure—the first metal manufacturer to earn such a label. ValSpar, the company which developed Fluropon Pure, was acquired by Sherwin-Williams in 2017.

"The contractor rearranged their sequence of construction three times while we were waiting for the metal panels. Without the contractor's cooperation that could never have happened. They wanted to do a Living Building Challenge project; they thought it was really important to the values of their company, too. It became a really huge endeavor, but we succeeded in the end."

PATTY KARAPINAR
Arch Nexus

"It was end of Thanksgiving holiday and we still didn't even have the metal panels on-site to skin the building. Kenner was looking at us and he's like, we have to be in by the end of the year and we don't even have windows on the building yet. We had tarps hanging from the parapet tied to the tree in the rain, installing all the metal panels in early December. We had to get those guys in."

SEAN KOTKE
MarketOne

REGENERATIVE RETROFIT: *California's First Living Building*

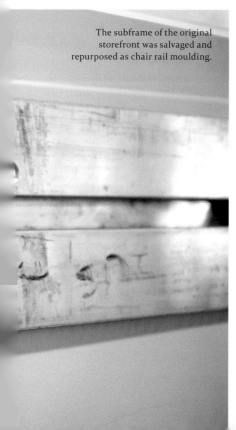

RETHINKING WASTE

To reduce environmental burdens from the extraction, processing, and disposal of materials, Imperative 14: Net Positive Waste states that all projects must feature at least one salvaged material per 500 square meters of gross building area or be an adaptive reuse of an existing structure.

The Imperative also sets minimum percentages for the diversion of materials from the landfill during construction.

The project team enthusiastically embraced the notion of conservation over waste management. Waste, they determined, is a human concept. Conservation and reuse became guiding principles, starting with the repurposing of the existing building.

Because it is an adaptive reuse project, Arch Nexus Sac satisfies the first part of Imperative 14. But the project team also took every opportunity to reuse and repurpose materials, including many from the existing building itself. The project incorporates fifteen distinct materials that were either salvaged from the existing building or site or acquired from elsewhere.

Lumber was carefully recovered, nails removed, and stacked; Kotke used much of it for blocking and backing in the new portions of framing. Plumbing fixtures were set aside and gifted to people as the need arose. Conduit was pulled out of the building and repurposed into a screen which shades a mechanical element at the building's rear entry, and for irrigation pipe sleeving. Insulation was reinstalled for thermal and acoustic control.

The spirit of salvaging infected the entire project team. One of the carpenters donated a beam he had been storing. Kotke offered a pile of salvaged bricks from his garage. Karapinar

was puzzling over what material to use to construct the exterior "green screen" when her husband, a retired SMUD employee, suggested they use pole steps that had been recovered from demolished power poles. The pole steps, which linemen use to scale power poles, became horizontal structural supports for the trellis.

At times, repurposed items found playful expression. A conference table from a previous office, though not beloved in its original form, was cut into strips and artistically arranged on the ceiling of the new conference room.

The lockers in the changing rooms were originally sourced from the fitness center which Arch Nexus had regenerated into their Salt Lake City office. They used some of the lockers in their Utah office but had been storing the extras.

The call for proposals for the bike rack sculpture underscored the team's passion for recycling. Artists were required to use repurposed materials, and Jay Stargaard and Deanna Marsh demonstrated in their innovative proposal that they were more than willing and able to take on this imperative. Stargaard utilized welding rods that she had been storing in her attic for over a decade; the wood for the benches came from slabs she had traded for from a salvage logging operation years before.

The subframe of the original storefront was salvaged and repurposed as chair rail moulding.

"Salvaging materials was probably one of the most fun parts of it for me. There's a lot of salvage in this building and part of it was trying to find as many creative ways as possible to use salvage. For one thing, it eased the Red List vetting."

PATTY KARAPINAR
Arch Nexus

"Sean and his team pulled every nail out of every piece of wood and we stacked it in a corner and left it there until it was time to go back and do new wood framing. The easier way would have been to just send it to the recycle yard and have them chop it up into wood chips. Instead we kept it there, right-sized it, and reused everything."

KENNY DEES
MarketOne

WASTE DIVERSION

From their experience on LEED projects, and because of California's strict building code standards, which mandate minimum recycling rates, MarketOne was already accustomed to diverting a high percentage of construction waste from the landfill.

However, the Living Building Challenge sets the bar much higher, requiring a recovery rate of 100 percent for soil and biomass, 99 percent for metal, paper, and cardboard, 95 percent for rigid foam, carpet, and insulation, and at least 90 percent for all others.

Sacramento boasts a robust recycling industry. Some facilities accept mixed debris boxes and guarantee at least a 70 percent diversion rate. MarketOne found industry partners who were willing to work with them and achieved an astounding overall waste diversion rate of 99 percent, thanks to the enthusiasm and cooperation of everyone who worked on the job.

The MarketOne team found that once they devised a system for separating lumber, drywall, metal, and other "waste" items on the front end, it was not any more difficult than comingling items in a combined debris bin. This experience spurred them to do much more "source separating" on subsequent projects.

The team did run into some challenges. One of the most difficult items to recycle was insulation. All of the used insulation from the

original building that was suitably clean was repurposed in the renovation; however, Kotke discovered they had material in excess of what they needed.

Kotke hit upon a potential solution: what if they "stored" the excess insulation in the stud cavities in the parapet walls on the roof? Although these walls were outside of conditioned space, it was a better option than sending the material to the landfill. And there was the hope that a future contractor would discover the insulation and either find a use for it or recycle it.

Thinking about products' end of life spurred the team to give preference to manufacturers with strong "take-back" and recycling programs. For example, Interface, which makes carpet tiles and other floor coverings, is dedicated to both product health and contributing to a circular economy. The company integrates recycled materials into its products and hosts a robust recycling program, recycling both face fibers and the backing from used carpet tiles into new products.

"My challenge on the Living Building Challenge was to find a place for some of this stuff, and to find people who could recycle it that typically don't."

SEAN KOTKE
MarketOne

"The contractor and the subcontractors and the carpenters would come up with ideas, which was really fun. It was contagious. Some of the contractors and subs and workers got excited about the Living Building Challenge instead of it just being like, oh my God, now we have to do all this other stuff that we don't usually have to do and it's a pain in the neck."

PATTY KARAPINAR
Arch Nexus

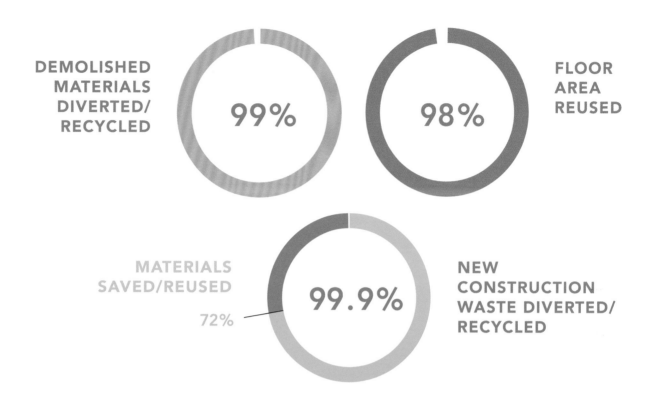

DEMOLISHED MATERIALS DIVERTED/ RECYCLED

99%

98%

FLOOR AREA REUSED

MATERIALS SAVED/REUSED

72%

99.9%

NEW CONSTRUCTION WASTE DIVERTED/ RECYCLED

SAVING BUILDINGS SAVES WASTE

According to the U.S. EPA, the United States generated 548 million tons of Construction and Demolition Debris, or C&D Debris, in 2015. The vast majority of that was from demolition, not new construction. "Recycling" a building comes with profound implications for conservation. It conserves virgin resources, preserves landfill space, and saves the embodied energy associated with extraction, manufacturing, and transportation.

By regenerating an old warehouse into a modern office, Arch Nexus greatly reduced the material and energy footprint of their project. The firm estimates that 98 percent of the building's original floor area was reused and that 72 percent of its materials (by surface area) were saved and incorporated into the new office. The vast majority of demolished materials were diverted from the landfill and recycled.

The team also thought ahead. It is likely that the regenerated building will not always serve as the professional office for a single architecture firm, and the interior layout was planned as such. The open plan could accommodate one, two, or even three tenants who would share common areas such as the bathrooms and kitchen.

The renovation was also designed and executed to facilitate recycling and reuse, should the building one day be deconstructed. For this reason, mechanical attachments were favored over adhesives or chemicals, and bolted connections over welded ones. Because toxic materials were minimized or in many cases eliminated, deconstruction and recycling will be easier and safer for future crews.

123

"If you have a process in place at the beginning, my opinion is that it is a little more time consuming, but not so extensive that you're going to go lose a job over it. A guy may need to think about putting wood in one dumpster versus drywall in another, but is he doing more work? Not necessarily; he's just thinking about his work in a different fashion. And that's where the whole team has to buy into it because one person can mess it up pretty easily."

KENNY DEES
MarketOne

"I found a place for just about everything. There was very little that we didn't recycle or reuse."

KENNY DEES
MarketOne

I said to Sean, "So you want to store it in the parapet,' and Sean said, 'Right. That's what I want to do.' I was like, that is genius. Someday, heaven forbid, someone's going to disassemble this building, and by then there might be a recycling path for fiberglass insulation. And when they find it in the parapet they can recycle it or reuse it somewhere else."

KENNER KINGSTON
Arch Nexus

"I did more reading on this project than on any project I've ever done, whether it was reading about products that were being brought into the building or making sure that what we were going to use was what they said. To actually see this stuff come to fruition—to see the rain catchment in action or a blossom of a fruit on the side of the building—it just changes your mindset as a builder."

SEAN KOTKE
MarketOne

•Declare.™

ECOS Concrete Sealer
Imperial Paints, LLC

Final Assembly: Spartanburg, SC, USA
Life Expectancy: >7 Years
End of Life Options: Landfill (100%)

Ingredients:

Vehicle: Water; **Binder:** Polymethyl Methacrylate, 2-Propenoic Acid Polymer With Ethenylbenzene Ammonium Salt; **Wetting Agent:** Poly(Oxy-1,2-Ethanediyl)-Hydro-Hydroxy-Ether With Fluoro (2-Hydroxyethyl)Poly(Difluoromethylene); **Defoamer:** Polyoxyethylated Stearyl Alcohol; **Preservative:** Methylisothiazolinone

Living Building Challenge Criteria:

IPA-0003	EXP. 09/01/2016
VOC Content: 0 g/L	VOC Emissions: CDPH Compliant
Declaration Status	■ LBC Red List Free
	☐ LBC Compliant
	☐ Declared

MANUFACTURER RESPONSIBLE FOR LABEL ACCURACY
INTERNATIONAL **LIVING FUTURE** INSTITUTE™ declareproducts.com

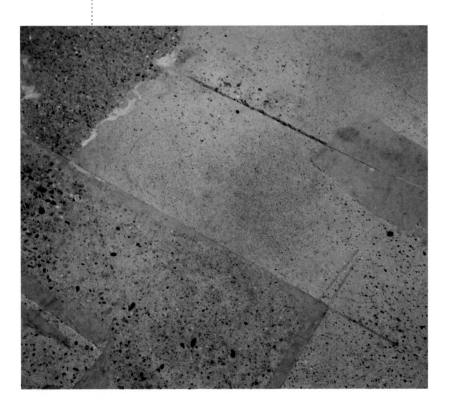

Declare.

Tufted Nylon on Graphlex backing

Interface

Final Assembly: Scherpenzeel, The Netherlands
Life Expectancy: 15 Years
End of Life Options: Take Back Program

Ingredients:

Calcium Carbonate, Type 6 Nylon (recycled) or Type 6,6 Nylon, Bitumen, Styrene butadiene rubber, Polyethylene terephthalate, Styrene butadiene styrene block copolymer, Polypropylene, Glass, Potassium formate, Acrylic resin, Starch, Aluminum hydroxide, Carbon black, Alcohol ethoxysulfate, Polyacrylic acid, Pigments*

*LBC Temp Exception I10-E4 Proprietary Ingredients

Living Building Challenge Criteria:

INT-0002	EXP. 4/01/2016
VOC Content: N/A	VOC Emissions: CDPH Compliant
Declaration Status	☐ LBC Red List Free
	☒ LBC Compliant
	☐ Declared

MANUFACTURER RESPONSIBLE FOR LABEL ACCURACY
INTERNATIONAL **LIVING FUTURE** INSTITUTE℠ declareproducts.com

Declare.

1600 Wall System™ 1 Curtain Wall and System™ 2 Curtain Wall
Kawneer Company, Inc.

Final Assembly: Springdale, AR, USA
Life Expectancy: 40+ Years
End of Life Options: Recyclable (90-98%), Landfill (2-10%)

Ingredients:

Frame: Aluminum; Thermal & Weathering: Ethylene Propylene Diene Terpolymer, Carbon Black, Kaolin, Dicumyl Peroxide, Zinc Oxide, Calcium Oxide, Calcium Carbonate, Polyethylene, Acrylonitrile Butadiene Styrene, Carbon Black; Fasteners: Stainless Steel

Living Building Challenge Criteria:

KAW-0003	EXP. 01 MAY 2018
VOC Content: N/A	VOC Emissions: N/A
Declaration Status	☒ LBC Red List Free
	☐ LBC Compliant
	☐ Declared

MANUFACTURER RESPONSIBLE FOR LABEL ACCURACY
INTERNATIONAL **LIVING FUTURE** INSTITUTE℠ declareproducts.com

The Materials Petal: **CONSERVATION AT THE CORE**

THE
EQUITY
PETAL

Promoting Dignity
and Accessibility for All

The intersecting circles of Luna Cycles, a public art installation and bicycle rack.

127

THE EQUITY PETAL
LIVING BUILDING CHALLENGE VERSION 3.0

PETAL INTENT

The intent of the Equity Petal is to transform developments to foster a true, inclusive sense of community that is just and equitable regardless of an individual's background, age, class, race, gender or sexual orientation. A society that embraces all sectors of humanity and allows the dignity of equal access and fair treatment is a civilization in the best position to make decisions that protect and restore the natural environment that sustains all of us.

PETAL IMPERATIVES

• Human Scale & Humane Places
• Universal Access To Nature And Place
• Equitable Investment
• JUST Organizations

128

"I am surprised by the impact and the connections the urban agriculture landscape at Arch Nexus has inspired within our R Street Corridor neighborhood. Whether it's witnessing a child observing a strawberry outside of a green plastic basket for the first time or an impromptu chat with a passerby regarding the timing of our blueberry harvest, the garden has helped build relationships with our neighbors in ways a typical urban landscape could not."

JENNIFER STYDUHAR
Arch Nexus

The intent of the Equity Petal is to encourage developments that foster a true, inclusive sense of community—one that is just and equitable regardless of a person's background, age, class, race, gender or sexual orientation.

129

When undertaking the Sacramento regeneration project, Arch Nexus took to heart the notion that even a private building has an impact on the community, and at its best should promote inclusivity and engagement. The requirements of the Equity Petal align with the goals of public interest design and SEED principles.

The Equity Petal: **PROMOTING DIGNITY AND ACCESSIBILITY FOR ALL**

A generous bench near the office entrance invites passersby to stop and rest.

Imperative 15: Human Scale and Humane places states that a project must be designed to create human-scaled places that promote human culture and human interactions.

The design elements at the corner of R and 10th Streets—the "parklet," the reoriented front entry, and the highly visible Design Lab—work together to convey these intentions. The parklet transformed a parking area into a pedestrian-friendly walkway that invites lingering and provides access to all. Framed in glass, the Design Lab provides a literal window into the creative activity taking place within and is in full view of passers-by. In addition to the bicycle rack sculpture, the design team added a bench and planter immediately adjacent the glass façade. Almost immediately, the bench became popular with people experiencing homelessness, who occasionally use both

the bench and the nook behind it as a sheltered, safe place to sleep. In addition, the edible fruits are not hidden behind the building, but grow in accessible locations adjacent the sidewalk, inviting passersby to sample them.

The Standard sets specific maximum (and sometimes minimum) requirements for paved areas, street and block design, building scale and signage, depending on the Transect. The design team was somewhat limited by the footprint of the existing building; however, the design reduced the paved parking area to 1,602 square feet, which represents just 11 percent of the total site area.

To comply with Imperative 16: Universal Access to Nature and Place, all sidewalk paving was replaced in order to ensure accessibility per the Americans with Disabilities Act (ADA).

REVITALIZING R STREET

R Street once served as a corridor for the Sacramento Valley Railroad, which began operating in 1856 and ran from the Sacramento River levee to the town of Folsom. A busy warehouse district thrived around the railroad before falling into decline in the 1950s.

The regeneration of R Street has not happened spontaneously, but was born of a deliberate vision and collaboration with the community. The R Street Corridor is a 27-block special planning district governed by a Master Plan which was first adopted in 1996. At that time, the district was characterized by distinctive historic brick buildings interspersed with vacant warehouses, commercial buildings, government offices, and empty lots. The vision was for a vibrant neighborhood with a deliberate focus on arts and culture and a mix of housing, retail, and commercial spaces.

The regeneration has occurred in phases. The portion of R Street between 10th and 13th Streets received a facelift in 2012, when broken asphalt was replaced and the distinctive arch and public art installations were added. Additional improvements on a three-block section to the north began a year later. A six-story warehouse was renovated into the Warehouse Artist Lofts in 2013, which today consists of 116 artist apartments above ground-floor commercial spaces and a restaurant.

Much of the focus has been on improving safety and accessibility for pedestrians and bicyclists. The projects have transformed the district into a popular, economically thriving neighborhood which has retained some of its gritty character and sense of history.

131

> *"JUST is a transparency label, not a certification program. The real reward is saying, here's who we are, here's how we're doing on gender diversity or local control. It's created these really great benchmarks."*

KENNER KINGSTON
Arch Nexus

> *"Before JUST, we felt like we were doing well across a wide range of social equity indicators. Now we know it and more importantly, our employees know it."*

KENNER KINGSTON
Arch Nexus

TRANSPARENCY AND EQUITY

Imperative 17: Equitable Investment states that for every dollar of total project cost, the development must donate half a cent or more to a charity or contribute to ILFI's Living Equity Exchange Program, which directly funds renewable infrastructure for charitable enterprises. Total project cost includes land, soft costs, hard costs, and systems furniture.

The donation target for the Arch Nexus SAC project was $29,365. To meet this requirement, Arch Nexus donated a total of $31,200 divided among eleven organizations.

In addition, Arch Nexus' exposure to the JUST program transformed the firm's approach to philanthropy.

Imperative 18: JUST Organizations requires that projects help facilitate the transformation to a more just and equitable society by collaborating with organizations which embrace transparency. At least one key project team member (Architect of Record, MEP Engineer of Record, or Structural Engineer of Record) must hold a JUST Label for their organization; project

teams must also send information about the JUST program to at least ten project consultants, sub-consultants or product suppliers.

JUST is a transparency platform created and hosted by the ILFI. Described by the ILFI as "a nutrition label for socially just and equitable organizations," it enables private companies, non-profits, government agencies, and other entities to transparently reveal facets of their internal operations, such as how they treat their employees and how and where they invest in their communities. The JUST platform utilizes twenty-two indicators organized under six categories: Diversity & Inclusion, Equity, Employee Health, Employee Benefits, Stewardship, and

> *"The authenticity offered by the JUST Program is helping the firm offer the kind of workplace that keeps employees committed for the long haul. The JUST roadmap to equity reminds us of areas needing improvement and allows us to celebrate our successes."*
>
> **KENNER KINGSTON**
> Arch Nexus

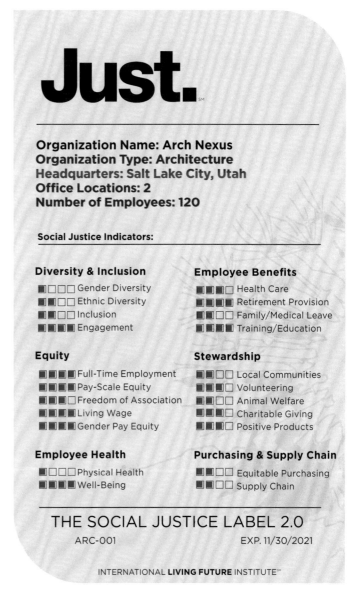

Just.

Organization Name: Arch Nexus
Organization Type: Architecture
Headquarters: Salt Lake City, Utah
Office Locations: 2
Number of Employees: 120

Social Justice Indicators:

Diversity & Inclusion
■□□□ Gender Diversity
■■□□ Ethnic Diversity
■■□□ Inclusion
■■■■ Engagement

Employee Benefits
■■■□ Health Care
■■■■ Retirement Provision
■■□□ Family/Medical Leave
■■■■ Training/Education

Equity
■■■■ Full-Time Employment
■■■■ Pay-Scale Equity
■■■□ Freedom of Association
■■■■ Living Wage
■■■■ Gender Pay Equity

Stewardship
■■□□ Local Communities
■■■□ Volunteering
■■■□ Animal Welfare
■■■□ Charitable Giving
■■■□ Positive Products

Employee Health
■□□□ Physical Health
■■■■ Well-Being

Purchasing & Supply Chain
■■□□ Equitable Purchasing
■■□□ Supply Chain

THE SOCIAL JUSTICE LABEL 2.0
ARC-001   EXP. 11/30/2021

INTERNATIONAL **LIVING FUTURE** INSTITUTE™

Purchasing & Supply Chain. (These are the categories and indicator metrics for JUST 2.0, which launched in 2019.) A simple one through four-star system is used to evaluate the organization on each indicator. The first star acknowledges the presence of a policy on a given topic; the next three are awarded for increasing performance levels.

When Arch Nexus started the Sacramento project, they did not have a JUST label. But they soon recognized that the program dovetailed with the firm's commitment to transparency and authenticity.

Shortly after launching the Arch Nexus SAC project in May of 2015, the company began the process of becoming a JUST-labeled organization, and by October they had earned their label, becoming the first organization in the Intermountain West and the first design firm in California to do so.

As a result, Arch Nexus has doubled down on equity. They have implemented a living wage, with entry-level rates of over $20 an hour in both Sacramento and Salt Lake City. In addition, the firm's employee-owners continuously build share value over time.

Arch Nexus has also found that having a JUST label is a valuable recruiting tool which draws potential employees who share the firm's values. Employee satisfaction has also spiked.

Arch Nexus is using their JUST label as a roadmap. The indicator metrics instruct them on where they are, so they can set goals for where they want to be. For example, although the Sacramento office employs slightly more women than men, gender diversity at the Salt Lake City office is not as equitable,

bringing the firm's overall rating down. Arch Nexus has made achieving greater equity in this area a priority.

Organizations must update their labels, at minimum, every two years. ILFI maintains a database for JUST-labeled organizations; anyone can access the database and view detailed information behind the ratings, as well as statements from the organization about how they are addressing each one.

The Equity Petal: **PROMOTING DIGNITY AND ACCESSIBILITY FOR ALL**

CHARITABLE ORGANIZATIONS TARGETED FOR EQUITABLE INVESTMENT IMPERATIVE

- Make-A-Wish Northern CA & Northern NV

- Loaves & Fishes

- The Road Home

- Big Brothers & Big Sisters of El Dorado County

- Habitat for Humanity Summit & Wasatch Counties

- Bicycle Collective

- Utah Rivers Council

- Heal Utah

- ILFI - Sacramento Collaborative

- ILFI - Great Basin Collaborative

- Kostopulos Dream Foundation

"Our passion for community stewardship is a key aspect of our company culture. Whether in the projects we design or in the causes we support, our purpose is to help elevate society through our influence on the built and natural environment. And because we see verbs where others see nouns, our Philanthropy Program is not just about financial support, it's about DOING."

ARCH NEXUS STATEMENT ON PHILANTHROPY

GIVING BACK

Arch Nexus' Philanthropy Program is deliberately built upon the JUST framework. It has two major components: charitable giving and a volunteer program.

Through the company's charitable giving program, Arch Nexus reinvests a percentage of its profits into programs that align with the company's purpose. Since earning a JUST label, Arch Nexus has increased the percentage of annual giving from 1 percent to 2 percent of profits. In addition to serving as a sponsor of the International Living Future Institute and hosting a university scholarship, the firm also gives to foundations such as Make-A-Wish and Foster Care.

Through its volunteer program, Arch Nexus offers each employee up to sixteen hours of paid time off each year to participate in volunteer activities. Half of these hours may be completed in the context of a coordinated, office-wide event. Employees pick the projects they deem most likely to regenerate communities.

In spring of 2019, Arch Nexus went a step further and launched Nexus Builds—the "action arm" of the firm's philanthropy program. Nexus Builds was conceived as a way to help staff gain practical, hands-on construction experience while directly confronting the problem of homelessness. Each year, the firm will select a community and build a tiny home for an individual or family who is currently without a permanent home.

TOWARDS GREATER EQUITY

As an ESOP, or employee-owned company, Arch Nexus had already committed to equity for its employees before acquiring a JUST label. Several institutional changes reflect the firm's growing evolution toward greater equity. For example, Arch Nexus went from holding corporate retreats to hosting company-wide retreats. The organization is unusually "flat"; of the one hundred twenty or so employees, twenty are principals. (More typically, a firm of this size will only have a small handful of principals.) Arch Nexus has also restructured its bonus program, moving from year-end bonuses to an Incentive and Accountability Program. Now, bonuses are awarded twice a year and are based on performance. The firm is reaping the benefits of this emphasis on equity, which includes the successful recruitment of talented young millennials.

135

The Equity Petal: PROMOTING DIGNITY AND ACCESSIBILITY FOR ALL

THE
BEAUTY
PETAL

Authentic Connections, Honest Beauty

930

The Beauty Petal: AUTHENTIC CONNECTIONS, HONEST BEAUTY

THE BEAUTY PETAL
LIVING BUILDING CHALLENGE VERSION 3.0

PETAL INTENT

The intent of the Beauty Petal is to recognize the need for beauty as a precursor to caring enough to preserve, conserve and serve the greater good. As a society, we are often surrounded by ugly and inhumane physical environments. If we do not care for our homes, streets, offices and neighborhoods, then why should we extend care outward to our farms, forests and fields? When we accept billboards, parking lots, freeways and strip malls as being aesthetically acceptable, in the same breath we accept clear-cuts, factory farms and strip mines.

.PETAL IMPERATIVES

• Beauty & Spirit
• Inspiration & Education

"*Biophilic design principles become the threads of the tapestry that hold the design together. When properly woven, these principles create beauty and spirit.*"

ARCH NEXUS WEBSITE

"*Spirit and meaning in design emerge from a deep understanding of place.*"

JASON F. MCLENNAN
Transformational Thought

The inclusion of the Beauty Petal is one of the more visionary aspects of the Living Building Challenge. It is an acknowledgment that building performance is not enough. Materials conservation is not enough. Even creating healthy buildings is not enough. If we want to create buildings that endure, and which bolster the human communities in which they are built, they must also be beautiful. Why? Because humans respond to beauty. If something is beautiful, we are more inclined to take care of it.

The Standard notes that beauty can serve "as a precursor to caring enough to preserve, conserve and serve the greater good."

Though beauty is certainly subjective, most people would agree that the modern human-built environment is not always a beautiful place. Too often, the "economic bottom-line" mentality prevails, and the human-built landscape is populated with utilitarian, trendy, and cheaply built structures and dominated by garish advertising. Whatever natural features remain are often smothered.

The Beauty Petal does not set standards for beauty, noting that "Mandating beauty is, by definition, an impossible task." Instead, project teams are asked to make an honest effort to incorporate beauty into their projects, in ways that are relevant and appropriate to the building's particular physical and cultural context.

Landscaping plants are beautiful for their own sake, but also connect to the site's ecology and natural history.

The Beauty Petal: AUTHENTIC CONNECTIONS, HONEST BEAUTY

Ferns on the Living Wall are a visible component of the building's greywater system.

THE BEAUTY OF AUTHENTICITY

Imperative 19: Beauty & Spirit states that "the project must contain design features intended solely for human delight and the celebration of culture, spirit and place appropriate to its function."

Arch Nexus took this Imperative to heart. By letting biophilic principles and an emphasis on place-based relationships guide the design, they created a building imbued with layers of meaning that at times may be sensed or felt more than explicitly understood. For instance, consider the dark band of metal which runs along the base of the building. In this case, design is being used to acknowledge the ecological importance of the historic floodplain. A person need not know why the dark band is there to appreciate it aesthetically or to have a sense of its rightness and rootedness. But learning the intention behind the design may spark a deeper appreciation of it, just as understanding the historical context and story behind a work of art inspires a more profound appreciation of its beauty.

Beauty can be a "hook." People who are first drawn in by the biophilic features at Arch Nexus SAC—the curving wall of living plants, or the playful bike rack—will likely be more open to hearing the project's sustainability story.

There are signs that Americans are starting to value materials that tell a story, and which have stood the test of time. The popularity of "distressed" wood flooring and reclaimed barn wood are two examples which hint at this evolution. Even if people do not necessarily stop to consider why weathered barn wood with nail holes and rust stains is so pleasing to the

> *"When it comes to green building and environmental performance, beauty and good design play an enormous role in the success of any project. In fact, aesthetics contribute to the overall effort in such significant ways primarily because people are involved and we are emotional beings."*

JASON F. MCLENNAN
Transformational Thought

eye, they may subconsciously be drawn to materials that seem authentic, and that tell a story about their past.

The design team deliberately sought out such materials for the Arch Nexus SAC regeneration. They also subjected each design and material choice to the litmus test of biophilia and place. As a result, there is nothing that is not necessary in the building. This is evidenced by a pared-down aesthetic which sends a clear message about the owners' values and priorities.

The exposed wood beams and preserved columns inside the building hint at its previous function as a warehouse. Marks from the carpenters left on the chair rail moulding speak of the craftsmanship of carpenters who handled the material decades before. Ink stains on the concrete floor tell of the building's previous incarnation as a print shop. The use of salvaged wood and metal sends a message that people valued these resources enough to find second and third lives for them. The reuse and regeneration of the building tells us that we can accommodate present needs and anticipate the future while honoring the past.

Learning the stories behind some of the salvaged and recycled materials may spark a deeper appreciation for the physical resources upon which we rely for our buildings and the effort and energy that goes into manufacturing them. And this can even prompt a shift in what we view as beautiful.

One could argue that this shift needs to happen—that cultural standards of beauty in the built environment need to change. Our notion of what is beautiful often stems from our values. If we only value what is shiny and new, that is what we will perpetuate. But if we value history, the conservation of precious resources, and hope for a thriving world for our children and grandchildren, then our perception of what is beautiful will necessarily expand.

> *"I never necessarily asked about window-to-wall ratio before; now I ask about it on every project. Before it was like, we like the look of glass. Now I ask of our designers, why are we doing that? Are we putting in glass because we like the look of it, or could we do something better? We owe it to our clients and we owe it as stewards of our profession to not perpetuate the bad choices."*

ROBB HARROP
Arch Nexus

> *"We had to sit back and ask why on every single thing. A lot of times the why is because it's cost effective or because it's what the client wants. On this project the why was because it was the right thing to do."*

HOLLI ADAMS
Arch Nexus

> *"This is an area that I think causes a really big challenge for the mainstreaming of this approach. There are a lot of people who are not even close to that mentality, who would look at something like the cracks on the floor and say, who screwed up? As opposed to seeing the real value and the foregone toxicity and the ability to generate power here. It's like you need different eyes to see the beauty that's inherent in the floor that's been repaired as opposed to papered over and pasted over with this noxious material."*

KATHLEEN AVE
SMUD

> *"Look at the use of barn wood. People pay exorbitant amounts of money for it. Barn wood is beautiful because it has been sitting out in some farmer's field for fifty years and then it got ripped down and someone decided to cut it up instead of throwing it away."*

SEAN KOTKE
MarketOne

A PLACE FOR PUBLIC ART

One of the requirements of the Beauty & Spirit Imperative is that the project should meaningfully integrate public art. Art is a reflection of where we are at a certain place and time. Public art humanizes the built environment, tells us a story about ourselves, and can help us understand a community's character. Public art also contributes to Equity, as it is available for the enjoyment of all, not just the private occupants of the building.

The R Street neighborhood already had an established tradition of playful and artistic bicycle racks. Arch Nexus decided to contribute one of its own, and commissioned a sculpture from local artists. Charlie Downs was involved with the Sacramento arts community, so he was charged with crafting the RFP and selecting the artists. One of the requirements was that the piece would be made of recycled materials and would comply with the Living Building Challenge, including the Red List.

Artists Jay Stargaard and Deanna Marsh were the perfect match for this project. Each had her own thriving practice and studio, but the two had also collaborated on projects before. They were drawn to the values embodied in the Living Building Challenge. Stargaard works exclusively with reclaimed metal she sources from scrap yards, dumps, and jobsites. Marsh works with metal and glass in a solar-powered studio, and her sculptures are informed by her understanding of natural cycles.

Downs' RFP stipulated that the piece needed to capture the essence of Sacramento, while also reflecting the values of Arch Nexus and the Living Building Challenge. Marsh and Stargaard and the other finalists were required to attend a presentation on the Living Building Challenge. They also toured the building site.

Stargaard and Marsh quickly developed the concept for a sculpture they called Luna Cycles. Five welded steel circles form the body of the bicycle rack. A metal railing threads through the "wheels," protecting people from the steep curb adjacent. The circles evoke the "history of motion" in the historic corridor. Vibrant stained glass elements, representing the phases of the moon, complement the steel circles and reinforce the cyclical themes.

Stargaard presented the design to the planning commission, but people were having trouble understanding the design on paper. She used black irrigation tubing to fashion several large circles, and set up the prototype in the planning office to show how the sculpture would function. She and Marsh won the commission.

Later on, Arch Nexus was having trouble finding signage that complied with the Red List, so they commissioned Stargaard to create custom signs for the building. When she presented her designs, they gave her suggestions for how they should be changed.

"I backed out of the project," says Stargaard. "What they were asking for wasn't going to look good, and I knew it wasn't what they really wanted."

"I said, I'm sorry, I forgot you were an artist; I was treating you like a fabricator," says Kingston. He promised Stargaard she would have complete artistic freedom if she returned to the project. She agreed, but under one condition: Arch Nexus staff would have to go indoor skydiving with her. Kingston and several other Arch Nexus employees accepted her offer.

"It's a wonderful teaching tool. We get people who come into the building and we'll walk through and they'll comment that this is a really beautiful building. And then they'll start noticing, there's no carpet on this floor; why didn't you do this? And it makes people start to think that you can still have a really beautiful building without doing all of these other things."

ROBB HARROP
Arch Nexus

"Part of the art is, what does it say? What is this beautiful object saying? I think one of the great things about having this building here is that it communicates to the public how important sustainability is. From a public expression of values, this building plays a really important and unique role here."

JENNIFER GRESS
California Air
Resources Board

INSPIRATION & EDUCATION

Imperative 20: Inspiration & Education sets forth a number of requirements for how project teams should disseminate information about the performance and operation of their Living Building.

Since conceiving the project, the team has been educating people about the Living Building Challenge and regenerative design in the Sacramento region and beyond. Their efforts continue to go well beyond the requirements of the Imperative.

Many of the project team have presented at conferences and workshops, at times reaching audiences outside of the "green building community." Having a Living Building in the community is a privilege and an opportunity. Leaders can point to it to demonstrate what is possible now, not in some distant future. Team members have engaged with the City of Sacramento and SMUD on a Living Building Challenge Accelerator, which has spawned over a dozen registered Living Building projects in the region. Arch Nexus staff have also participated in the Mayors' Commission on Climate Change.

Arch Nexus has enjoyed the unique opportunity of not only educating the public, but themselves, as occupants of the building they own and operate. In addition to InHABIT, the gamified platform that helps educate and engage Arch Nexus employees about how their actions impact the performance of the building, staff learn from their everyday experiences while occupying a Living Building. Staff directly see the consequences of their actions, whether composting kitchen scraps, washing dishes, or bicycling to work. They experience firsthand how operating windows affects comfort, indoor air quality, and energy usage. This in turn is making them better design professionals, ones who can understand and anticipate the challenges their clients are likely to face, and steer them toward greater accountability and environmental stewardship while creating buildings that promote healthier, happier occupants.

145

REGENERATIVE RETROFIT: *California's First Living Building*

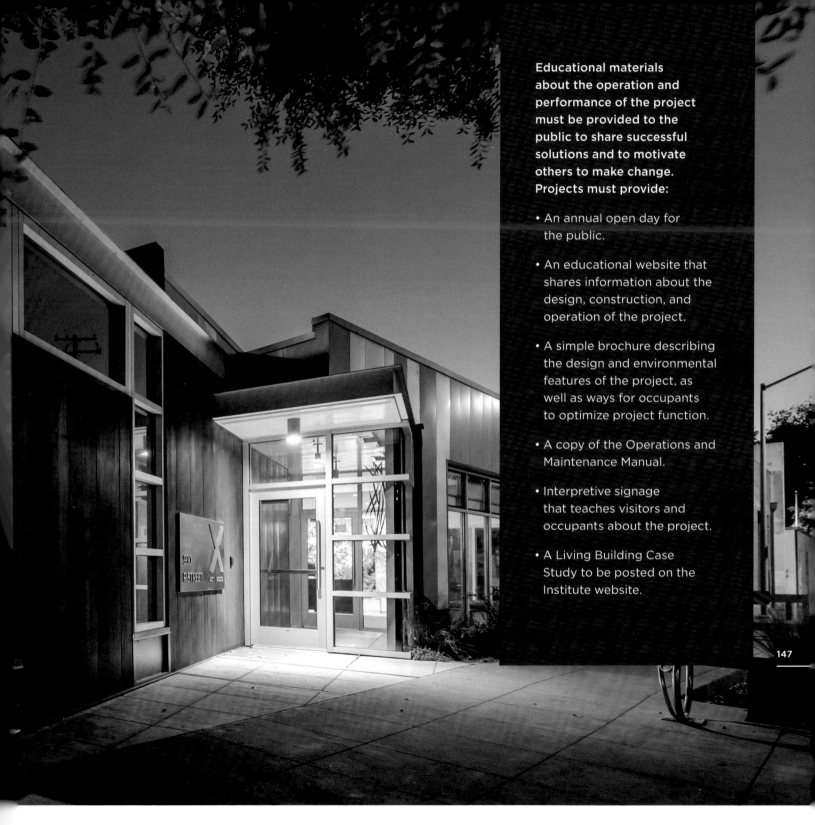

Educational materials about the operation and performance of the project must be provided to the public to share successful solutions and to motivate others to make change. Projects must provide:

- An annual open day for the public.

- An educational website that shares information about the design, construction, and operation of the project.

- A simple brochure describing the design and environmental features of the project, as well as ways for occupants to optimize project function.

- A copy of the Operations and Maintenance Manual.

- Interpretive signage that teaches visitors and occupants about the project.

- A Living Building Case Study to be posted on the Institute website.

147

The Beauty Petal: AUTHENTIC CONNECTIONS, HONEST BEAUTY

PART IV

Performance

Owning, Occupying,
and Operating a Living Building

148

Occupant behavior has a significant impact on energy consumption and on the functioning of the building's water systems.

149

Annual block parties encourage
R Street neighbors to mingle.

Construction on the Arch Nexus SAC building had commenced in March of 2016. Arch Nexus took occupancy of the building on Friday, December 30, 2016, the last business day of the year.

Arch Nexus now enjoyed an unusual opportunity: the chance to occupy and operate one of the world's few Living Buildings, and one that they owned and had designed. They also intended to prove the point that occupant behavior can significantly impact how a building performs.

To earn certification, Living Building projects must undergo a twelve-month performance period and a third-party audit. They began the performance period right away, in January of 2017.

In March, Sacramento staff held a ribbon cutting and, along with their R Street neighbors, hosted a block party to officially celebrate their opening. Shortly thereafter, the project began attracting awards and accolades, as organizations began to recognize what the Arch Nexus SAC team had accomplished. In October of 2017, Engineering News-Record (ENR) California named Arch Nexus SAC the best Green Project for 2017; in January of 2018, the ENR National announced Arch Nexus SAC as the winner of the prestigious Green Project of the Year award. In April of 2018, Arch Nexus SAC officially became the world's 19th Living Building.

> *"We deployed a low-energy USB fan at each desk to recognize that we have a higher-than-average cooling set point. Here's a two-watt way of addressing that."*
>
> **KENNER KINGSTON**
> Arch Nexus

HIGH-PERFORMANCE OCCUPANTS

By the end of the performance year, Arch Nexus SAC had produced 179 percent of the energy it had consumed.

In general, the solar array produced as much or more energy than was predicted. Not surprisingly, production peaked in the summer months and fell off during the winter, with its shorter daylight hours.

Kingston had expected the building to overproduce by about 120 percent. To ensure the building would produce at least 105 percent of the energy it consumed, the energy modeler and solar installer had each added a "safety factor" to their predictions; Arch Nexus had also factored in another contingency for weather.

Still, the energy model had predicted an Energy Use Intensity, or EUI, of 36 kBtu/sf/year. The actual EUI was slightly over 26. Month after month, energy consumption was well below what had been predicted.

The difference, Kingston is certain, is the occupants. Kingston credits the InHABIT platform with training and engaging occupants so that they clearly understand their role in reducing energy usage. He estimates that staff in the Sacramento office are using 26 percent less energy than expected in an already high-performance building.

There is some automation, to be sure. When the last person leaves the office they set the security alarm, which automatically turns off all discretionary loads within the building. The

building manager can also set the alarm remotely using a smartphone. The already efficient HVAC system is also programmed with nighttime setbacks—for example, in winter, the nighttime temperature is lower than it is during occupied hours; in summer, it is higher. That said, staff control many aspects of the building. They turn lights on and off manually and they decide when to open windows and shut off the HVAC system. If a person feels too warm, each workstation is equipped with a small personal fan powered via a USB cable connection.

The EUI has stayed in the range of 26 year after year, proving that the performance period was not a fluke.

"You can create high-performance buildings, and you can create high-performance occupants," says Kingston. "You just have to train them, engage them, and give them the knowledge they need."

Arch Nexus has acquired ownership of the InHABIT platform. As of this writing, they are using the application to engage occupants in their Salt Lake City office as they prepare to recertify the building for LEED for Existing Buildings and explore some level of Living Building Challenge certification. They have also made InHABIT available to other businesses and organizations and they have deployed the platform in both the public and private sector, including higher education.

POSITIVE FEEDBACK

Every week during the performance period, occupants received feedback on energy consumption and production via the whole building utility meter.

They also had access to sub-meter data, which broke down energy use by end-use category: Server, Plug Load, Lighting, Pumps, HVAC and EV Car Charger. This detailed feedback showed employees how much energy they were using and how that use changed over time. For instance, they could note the drop-off in HVAC energy use in spring, as the weather grew more pleasant and staff started opening windows more frequently.

Several of the categories remained steady throughout the performance period or fluctuated as predicted. For example, it took more energy to keep the server room cool during the summer months even though the set point of 80 degrees remained the same throughout the performance period. It is worth noting that the computer server was by far the greatest single source of energy consumption.

Efficient fans at each workstation
help keep cooling energy low.

Actual energy use has consistently fallen well below what was predicted, thanks in large part to the building's occupants. Note that the computer server comprises the largest category of energy use.

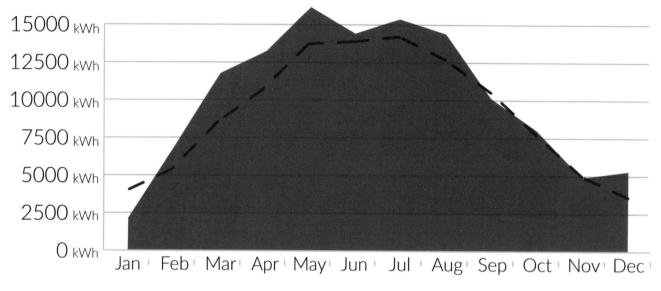

ENERGY PRODUCTION

 PREDICTED - - -

ACTUAL

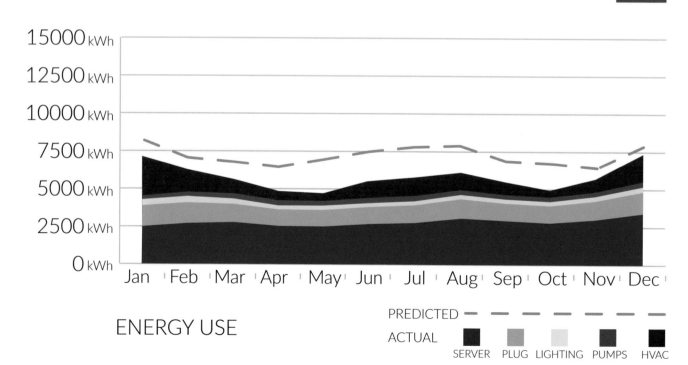

ENERGY USE

PREDICTED - - -

ACTUAL   SERVER   PLUG   LIGHTING   PUMPS   HVAC

"Our culture has come to expect automation. You walk into a building and everything just happens; there is no active stewardship in terms of the human relationship with the building. With Kenner's leadership, we've flipped that on its head. The building is not the thing that's going to make the big difference. It's what the people do with the building. The building is a tool. And how the people engage with buildings is absolutely critical."

BRIAN CASSIL
Arch Nexus

Several tweaks in the operation of the building affected energy consumption during the performance period. For example, in early March McBride activated the vampire switch for the first time, which meant that computer printers and other equipment were no longer "sipping" energy after business hours. Baseline plug load energy use immediately decreased.

Also in March, the Sacramento staff decided to switch from occupancy sensors to vacancy sensors. Occupancy sensors switch lights on when a person's presence is detected, but the sensors were keeping lights on longer than was needed, especially in the office restrooms. Vacancy sensors require a person to manually switch on the light; if the person forgets to switch it off, the vacancy sensor does so once no movement is detected. But mostly, employees simply started switching lights on and off, just as they did at home. This simple change caused lighting energy to drop. Days were also getting longer at this time, so staff were less reliant on artificial lighting, and although lighting energy increased slightly in the fall, it never reached the same level as when the occupancy sensors were in use.

Once the vampire switch was activated, McBride discovered that the composting control panel, which was tied to the plug load panel, was switching off every night. This was turning off the pumps for the leachate and resetting the fans to a lower mode. McBride then ran an extension cord to connect the composting control panel to the pump load panel. Although this change caused pumping energy to increase slightly, it ensured that the leachate pumps and fans would remain online when the vampire switch disabled the building's plug loads.

155

"Natalie is very particular about ordering lunches from places that she knows will package the food per her request. When she orders large lunches for our whole office she makes sure to specify that the food is packaged in aluminum pans that we can either reuse or recycle. It really helps us reduce the amount of plastic waste."

ERICA MCBRIDE
Arch Nexus

"Everyone in our office was pretty engaged in recycling and waste reduction from the beginning. InHABIT played a big part in that."

ERICA MCBRIDE
Arch Nexus

Hank is a vital part of the Arch Nexus SAC food composting system.

WASTING NOT

Arch Nexus tracks waste and recycling for both of their offices. Employees recycle paper, aluminum, glass, batteries, tin, and they compost food scraps, napkins, and coffee filters. Any compost that isn't used in the landscaping is taken home by a staff member who uses the compost for their chickens.

During the performance period, staff achieved a waste diversion rate of 82 percent, saving nearly four thousand pounds of paper, aluminum, and kitchen scraps from the landfill. Packaging and containers that cannot be recycled make up the bulk of the office's trash.

McBride credits InHABIT with encouraging and reminding staff to recycle instead of throwing items into the trash, but she also sends out reminders when she discovers issues that need addressing. She has also recruited staff to participate in waste audits, which encourage deeper engagement and awareness of what people were actually putting in their waste and recycle bins.

Just as important, employees try to avoid single-use and disposable plastic packaging whenever possible. The kitchen is stocked with durable dishes and cutlery and cloth napkins, and staff patronize restaurants that are willing to package food as requested. Staff can also take reusable containers with them when they go out to lunch.

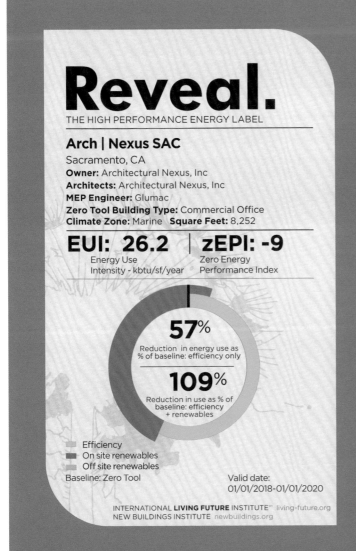

PERFORMANCE, REVEALED

In early 2018, Arch Nexus SAC became the first building in the California Central Valley to obtain a Reveal Label from the International Living Future Institute (ILFI). Reveal is a tool which communicates information about a building's energy efficiency and renewable energy production in a simple graphic format. Crunching twelve months of verified energy consumption data, the label rates energy performance on three metrics: energy use intensity (EUI), zero energy performance index (zEPI), and energy use reduction from baseline.

EUI is expressed as energy per square foot per year and is calculated by dividing the total energy consumed by the building in one year (measured in kBtu or GJ) by the total gross floor area of the building. Different building types have different average EUI values; for example, a hospital is much more energy intensive than a warehouse. Even within the office category, large offices tend to have a higher EUI than small ones. This is why it is important to compare buildings of the same type. With a EUI of 26.2, Arch Nexus SAC uses 57 percent less energy than an average office building in the United States, according to the EPA's ENERGY STAR Portfolio Manager.

The zero energy performance index (zEPI) is the ratio of energy performance of the rated building to the average energy consumption of a similar building based on the 2003 Commercial Buildings Energy Consumption Survey (CBECS) data that is operated in a similar climate, for similar hours, and in similar operating conditions.

"I was really surprised at the connection between social science and architecture. The occupant engagement zone of practice is really important, especially as it relates to expressing to clients that we understand their operational problems. It's not all about the building. There's more to it than that; the building and the occupants have to work together."

KENNER KINGSTON
Arch Nexus

"The real story here is efficient occupants. The fact that they use 25 percent less energy than predicted is a big deal."

KENNER KINGSTON
Arch Nexus

"One of the things that I noticed during the post-occupancy surveys that Arch Nexus did is that daylight sensors never work. I didn't find one building where the daylight sensors were actually doing what they're supposed to do, and that includes our own building in Salt Lake City. In Sacramento the lights are off almost all the time. But I don't think that's because of the daylight sensors. I think it's because of the occupants."

BRIAN CASSIL
Arch Nexus

158

A minor revision of the original office plan entailed the removal of two enclosed offices and opened up the space even more.

RETHINKING OFFICE SPACE

When the Arch Nexus SAC office was being designed, the team followed the precedent established at the Salt Lake City office that every senior principal has an enclosed office.

There were three senior principals at Arch Nexus at the time; hence, the design called for three enclosed offices. They decided to place these in the center of the space, where they would separate the two Neighborhoods without blocking views out the windows.

Providing these offices with access to fresh air was a challenge. The original design called for glass on both the front and back, but the glass storefront systems were expensive. Kingston reluctantly deleted the glass; instead, each was fitted with a single glass door and sidelight. The only way to ensure natural ventilation was through a skylight with integrated ventilation. But the products did not work as anticipated.

By late 2018, two of the senior partners had retired, and the third had transferred to Salt Lake City. It was clear the offices were not working for anyone in their current configuration. Toward

the end of 2018, the interior designer and architectural designer Peter McBride suggested that one of the offices be removed and converted into an interior materials library. The two remaining could be revamped as "hoteling" offices that anyone could use.

Over the winter holidays MarketOne returned and launched a small remodel. The project was executed according to the Living Building Challenge; all products and materials were vetted for the Red List, and the doorframes were made from studs that were removed from the third office.

Today, the two offices are daylit with Solatubes and fitted with glass doors on both sides, facilitating natural ventilation. Any staff member can check them out.

159

THE NEW NORMAL

By March of 2018, Arch Nexus SAC had finally passed the final indoor air quality test. Staff had also learned to check outdoor air quality before opening windows.

That summer ushered in an especially bad fire season throughout the West, and particularly in California. Large fires broke out in Shasta and Mendocino Counties in July. But the worst was yet to come.

In November of 2018, the Camp Fire devastated the town of Paradise, ninety miles north of Sacramento. For a time, air quality in Northern California was the worst in the world. Toxic smoke from this fire blew directly into the Sacramento Valley. A sickly brown cloud hung over the city. Air quality ranked as Hazardous; at one point, fine particulate matter exceeded 400 micrograms per cubic meter of air. Schools closed, and fire stations distributed free dust masks.

At Arch Nexus SAC, employees were keeping the windows shut tight. But something was desperately wrong.

"Staff called and said, 'It's the apocalypse in here right now; the smoke in the building is starting to burn our eyes,'" recalls Kingston.

Smoke was getting inside the well-sealed and insulated building. But how?

The three enclosed offices in the center of the space had not yet been remodeled. An examination of the ventilated skylights revealed that the fabric "sock" which connected the ceiling diffuser to the roof had fallen away: smoke was literally pouring into the building. McBride corrected the problem, and once the offices were remodeled and the ventilated skylights replaced with Solatubes, the issue was fixed permanently.

Unfortunately, larger and more devastating wildfires appear to be the "new normal" in California, and people who live in wildfire-prone regions will have to adapt. Such fires are also revealing the consequences of the toxic chemicals and materials so prevalent in building products today. Lead, asbestos, plastic, furniture, electronics, hazardous chemicals, pesticides stored in garages—all of these burn and release gases and particles into the air and soil. In some cases, water sources have been contaminated. In Paradise, residents were not allowed to return until the hazards had been mitigated. Sadly, such episodes only highlight the importance of avoiding these materials and products, for the health of us all.

Today, Arch Nexus staff still consult Spare the Air to make sure the air quality index is acceptable before opening the windows. The PM 2.5 level must be below 15; if it is not, staff may not operate windows, even if the indicator light signals favorable conditions for natural ventilation. They also keep a supply of dust masks on hand for staff and their families for the next time outdoor air quality deteriorates.

The Camp Fire erupted on November 8, 2018, and quickly raged into the foothill town of Paradise.

> *"The Living Wall is probably the most important element of the building in terms of its cross-functions. It's dealing with beauty, biophilia, and place, but most importantly, it's a key part of the water reuse system. The Living Wall is the final path for greywater; without it, we'd overflow into the sewer every day."*

KENNER KINGSTON
Arch Nexus

TUNING THE WATER SYSTEMS

Arch Nexus staff quickly learned to work with the composting toilets and greywater system; in fact, staff report that they enjoy observing the interactive relationships with these systems—how their actions impact the quantity and quality of greywater, for instance. And although these systems have functioned as designed, they have required some minor tweaking.

THE RIGHT BALANCE OF PLANTS: Soon after occupancy, landscape architect Jennifer Styduhar noticed that although some of the plants in the Living Wall were thriving, many others languished. Upon the recommendation of a professional indoor landscape consultant, they removed most of the plants and replaced them with others. But these new plants also failed to thrive. Styduhar and building manager Erica McBride began working together to solve the problem. They learned that the plants, chosen for their aesthetics and ability to evaporate greywater, were not adapted to the relatively high level of salts in it. These salts are mainly a byproduct of the soap Arch Nexus staff was using to wash dishes. McBride swapped the powdered product for a gel, and while this helped, it did not eliminate the problem.

PLANTS IN THE LIVING WALL

Boston Fern

Heart Leaf Philodendron

Blue Star Polypodium

Stag Fern

Plumosa Fern

161

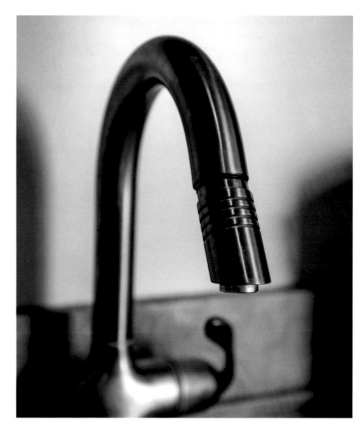

After some research, McBride and Styduhar replaced most of the plants with more salt-tolerant species. In fact, only two of the original species, Heart Leaf Philodendron and Blue Star Polypodium, remain in the wall today. They also started adding an organic fertilizer to the treated greywater, along with a Bushdoctor Sledge Hammer, a product which helps break down and flush out salts. Finally, they implemented a cleaning regime, siphoning out the reservoir tank and replenishing it with fresh treated greywater once a month.

KEEPING THE GREEN OUT OF GREYWATER:
The greywater system was designed to continuously recirculate the water through the treatment components to prevent stagnation. However, a problem arose soon after occupancy.

Greywater from all of the drains in the building flows into a large submersible pump, which is slightly elevated on a tray in the floor. The float on the pump is set at the lowest level possible, but it does not activate until greywater in the basin reaches a level of about six inches.

Because the building is not typically occupied over the weekend, no new greywater enters the system for over two days, which means the sump pump does not activate during that time. After about twenty-four hours, any stagnant greywater left in the basin begins to support algae growth. McBride purchased "bubblers" similar to those used in fish tanks to aerate the greywater, which has helped the problem somewhat. She also recruits staff to help clean the basin at least twice a year.

There are plans to modify the sump and pump so that no greywater remains between pump cycles, which will match the intent of the original design.

THE ROLE OF OCCUPANTS: Arch Nexus employees soon learned that the way they use water in the building affects both the quantity and quality of their greywater. For example, if more people bike to work and shower at the office, the volume of greywater increases. Any chemicals, soap, or food scraps that go down the drain end up in the greywater system. From the beginning, staff were careful to use non-toxic products, including the prohibition of hand sanitizers, which kill beneficial bacteria. But working with a greywater system required making some other changes as well. At one point, McBride noticed the greywater was discolored. Staff were using a durable copper coffee filter to conserve resources, and the coffee grounds were staining the greywater. They switched to unbleached, biodegradable paper filters which do not need rinsing. Similarly, they began using compostable napkins to wipe off plates before rinsing them. The coffee filters, compostable napkins, and food scraps are composted and then become food for the urban agriculture plants outside.

COMPOSTER COMPLEXITIES

As with the greywater system, Arch Nexus occupants have been learning how to work with the composting toilets. One episode illustrates the close observation and attention that is required to manage these "living" systems.

One Monday, McBride entered the composting room and found it infested with fungus gnats. She soon realized that the fans had stopped running.

Each composting unit comes equipped with a fan which helps evaporate liquid and eliminate odors and a pump which transports leachate from the bottom of the unit to the top. Both the fan and the pump run off the same power supply. The fans were set at the highest speed so they could evaporate as much leachate as possible; however, the power supply could not accommodate both the pump and the fan at high speed.

Normally, when the pump activates, the fan shuts off temporarily. Only in this case, the fans and pumps had stopped communicating correctly. The fans were shutting off, but they were not coming back on.

After a couple of days of troubleshooting, McBride adjusted each fan so that it was running at half-speed; this way, the power supply could accommodate both the fan and the pump simultaneously, and the fans would never shut off.

Another related issue was resolved several months later. The fans in the composting room were pulling in too much air from the rest of the office, "competing" with the building's main ventilation system and creating a slight negative pressure within. Capital Engineering came up with a simple solution. New duct work was installed to re-route air from the restroom and battery room exhaust fans to make up the air in the composting room. Filter boxes ensure that the exhaust air is filtered to MERV 13 standards. These adjustments not only brought the internal pressure back to neutral, but improved indoor air quality by a few measurements.

"Because of his role in creating this energy-efficient computer system, our IT specialist found himself in his IT room in Salt Lake talking to a room of three hundred people about the computer system. The Living Building Challenge is now working its way through this building through Kent to a new audience. Who could have possibly imagined that the program would touch that audience?"

BRIAN CASSIL
Arch Nexus

THE RIPPLE EFFECT

Like every Living Building Challenge project, Arch Nexus SAC has influenced everyone who worked on the project. For the architects, designers, builders, engineers and other craftspeople, the experience has impacted not only their professional practices, but their daily habits and choices, and how they think about waste, energy, water, and materials.

At work, even if you cannot convince every client to take on the Living Building Challenge, you can promote practices which emphasize efficiency, equity, and health.

At home, even if your home is not a Living Building, you can still choose healthy products over toxic ones. You can still choose to save water and energy, to reuse materials, and to compost kitchen scraps rather than throw them away.

As an advocate, you have a chance to reach new, sometimes unexpected audiences, whether a classroom of eight-year-olds or a room full of IT experts.

You have the opportunity to plant seeds, and at least some of these will take root and bear fruit.

A LIVING DEVELOPMENT IN MOAB

While in the lunch line at a conference, Arch Nexus partner Peter Moyes met Emily Niehaus, the founder of Community Rebuilds, a non-profit general contractor focused on creating affordable housing in certain communities in Utah and Colorado.

Community Rebuilds had been wanting to create a small development of Living Buildings in Moab to house the program's student interns, but they had not been able to find an experienced local architect to help guide them through the process. After the initial meeting, a partnership with Arch Nexus quickly developed.

Community Rebuilds targets tourist economies where housing costs are high. Their Moab homes cost around $70 per square foot, half the cost of standard construction in the region. They are able to keep costs down through low-carbon construction and student labor. Designs are kept simple, and the straw-bale homes are built with low-cost natural materials and incorporate salvaged, recycled, and donated materials wherever possible. Students build one to two homes during six-month internships in exchange for room, board, and training.

Arch Nexus led a regenerative design workshop in September of 2018, and the project launched to build four straw-bale homes to Living Building Challenge standards.

"We get to learn about straw bale construction, and we get to teach them how to convert their existing housing product into a Living Building," says Kingston.

In February of 2019, interns began carefully deconstructing an existing bunkhouse on the Mill Creek site. Much of the salvaged materials will be used in the new buildings.

The first two homes are slated to be completed in spring of 2020. They will likely be the first Certified Living Buildings in the state of Utah.

ONE HOUSE AT A TIME

Community Rebuilds is a 501(c)3 nonprofit corporation whose mission is to build energy-efficient housing, provide education on sustainability, and improve the housing conditions of the workforce through an affordable program.

Community Rebuilds launched in Moab in 2010, and after a few successful projects, expanded to Colorado. At the time of this writing, they have completed thirty-six homes and trained two hundred fifty budding professionals.

Community Rebuilds Living Buildings at Mill Creek in Moab features:

- Passive solar design

- Highly insulating straw bale wall construction

- Heavy focus on salvaged material

- Materials with low embodied carbon footprint

- Composting toilet systems

- Rainwater collected and stored for toilet flushing and irrigation

- Greywater reuse for agriculture

- Permaculture landscape design

- Earthen plaster finishes throughout the interior, including adobe floors

- Lime plastered exterior walls

- Solar PV array that will offset all annual energy use

165

"Nexus Builds has been fantastic for recruitment and retention. It helps create a different culture. We grew internally, but we also grew externally. That was not something that I expected"

CHERYL MCMURTRY
Arch Nexus

"Overall it was a great day! It was wonderful to be outside, working with awesome people, and constructing a project that will have a positive impact in someone's life."

JESSICA PETERSEN
Arch Nexus

166

THE BLOCK PROJECT WEBSITE

NEXUS BUILDS A LIVING BUILDING

In 2019, Arch Nexus partnered with The BLOCK Project and built a 125-square-foot home to Living Building Challenge standards as part of their company-wide volunteer program, Nexus Builds.

The BLOCK Project is a collaboration between BLOCK Architects and Facing Homelessness, a media project turned non-profit. The project was conceived to provide a tangible solution to homelessness in the City of Seattle while breaking down barriers between people experiencing homelessness and other residents. Hence, it is both a housing initiative and a community building project.

Architects Rex Hohlbein and Jenn LaFreniere designed the BLOCK home. Though tiny, each home is completely self-sufficient and includes a greywater system, composting toilet, and small solar PV array. Design details include a generous covered porch and outdoor storage area. Finish-grade plywood helps create a beautiful and warm interior, and a rolling bed frees up space.

The ultimate goal is to place a BLOCK home in at least one backyard in every residentially-zoned block in the city. Each home will house an individual or family who is currently experiencing homelessness. So far, over one hundred Seattle homeowners have offered to host a BLOCK home.

One hundred percent of the labor for building the homes is donated by general contractors, subcontractors, and community volunteers. Arch Nexus built their BLOCK Home at their Salt Lake City office. A dedicated construction yard was carved out of the existing parking lot, and a portion of the interior office was dedicated to storage. Everyone in the firm was invited to participate. Staff could choose when and how to contribute, and Sacramento employees were flown to the site for two-day work stints. Construction began in March 2019. The home, which was the ninth BLOCK Home to be completed, was delivered to the host family in Seattle on November 2, 2019. Arch Nexus is partnering with Miller Hull and Herrera to ensure their project achieves full Living Building Challenge certification, and they will stay engaged with the host family and the occupant throughout the performance period.

For Arch Nexus, participating in The BLOCK Project gave staff the opportunity to live their values while gaining practical, hands-on construction skills—experience which will ultimately help them become better architects and designers. Participating employees have also gained practical experience with the Living Building Challenge. Arch Nexus can now claim to be the only organization in the world to have designed, owned, operated, and built a Living Building.

In 2019, Arch Nexus held an internal design competition so they could develop their own tiny home prototype. The designs focused on mobility, flexibility and simplicity. In 2020, Arch Nexus intends to partner with a local organization and build a tiny home for a community member closer to home.

> *"When the project was completed and Arch Nexus finally moved in, it struck me that we should not just move on to the next project. We needed to do something more to try to amplify the results and to attract more people, more projects in the pipeline."*

KATHLEEN AVE
SMUD

> *"Because California is so much more progressive than a lot of the states that we work in, we thought that in rooting for Sacramento we would get to harvest knowledge and opportunity and move it back to other locations like Salt Lake City or Boise or our projects on the Colorado plateau. And it has really worked out very well in that regard."*

KENNER KINGSTON
Arch Nexus

A GOOD NEIGHBOR

Arch Nexus has been involved in the Sacramento community for decades. Staff have served on the planning commission and on the boards of non-profit organizations such as Make-A-Wish, MESA, and the Sacramento Regional Builders Exchange CREATE Mentoring Program.

The process of designing and building a Living Building has yielded rich partnerships, such as the ones with Sutter Middle School and SMUD. Owning and operating a building in the R Street Neighborhood has enabled Arch Nexus to participate even more deeply in community life.

"Community was part of the vision," says Cheryl McMurtry, Business Development Associate for Arch Nexus. "It's not just our office; the building also supports and serves our community."

Arch Nexus offers the facilities for community meetings, from corporate retreats to small business luncheons. Various organizations, including the City's planning commission, Metro EDGE, SMUD, and the R Street Sacramento Partnership board, have held meetings at Arch Nexus SAC. Local artists have shown art within the building, and local photographers have used the building for wedding photography.

168

169

"Despite social media, information does not travel efficiently. And that's why we did the Accelerator, to try to galvanize some of the energy around this project and to put Sacramento on the map and not concede to the Bay Area or LA as being kind of a leading area for a Living Future."

KATHLEEN AVE
SMUD

"SMUD is a very regular established partner with the city, whereas a project team is a temporary partner. Having an ongoing partner be a connector gives the city a pathway to continue its own work."

JENNIFER GRESS
California Air Resources Board

"With the Accelerator, SMUD created a funding mechanism to help introduce teams or projects or owners that wouldn't otherwise be pursuing these goals to these ideas. As a result we were able to contact the city and Perkins + Will, the planning firm that was planning the Sacramento Valley Station, and say, let us give you a free Living Community Challenge charrette. All you have to do is come with an open mind."

KENNER KINGSTON
Arch Nexus

"It was an incredibly interesting process of just putting it out there and seeing who shows up and who wants to do this kind of work. It's a magnet for the most motivated people—these are the people who want to spend the money and who want to do the best work they can do."

KATHLEEN AVE
SMUD

THE LIVING FUTURE PROJECT ACCELERATOR

Over the course of the Arch Nexus SAC project, Sacramento Municipal Utility District, or SMUD, had become a valued partner and advocate for the Living Building Challenge.

As the project wound down, SMUD Senior Climate Program Manager Kathleen Ave wanted to capitalize on the momentum and excitement it had generated. She wondered if there was a way to fast-track Living Building Challenge projects in the region and build on the work that the Sacramento Collaborative was already doing.

Ave met Brad Liljequist, the International Living Future Institute's Director of Zero Energy at the time, at a conference. As they talked, Ave realized they shared a common passion. Liljequist described a project in the Puget Sound area which had aimed to recruit and encourage Living Building Challenge projects. Working with a small infusion of cash from the Boeing Foundation, they identified potential candidates, then reached out and offered support, whether financial assistance or help with paperwork. Through this effort they were able to register half a dozen projects. Ave, Liljequist, and Kingston met in Sacramento and planned how to expand upon this model through a series of classes, building tours, and technical and financial support. SMUD agreed to fund the effort.

The Living Future Project Accelerator launched with three classes in the fall of 2017. The classes were open to the public and focused on different aspects of the Living Building framework. Complementing each class was a building tour of Arch Nexus SAC or a local net-zero energy project.

Afterwards, staff from Arch Nexus and ILFI made themselves available for consulting sessions and technical support to project developers who wanted to undertake the Living Building Challenge. Arch Nexus organized and participated in a design charrette for the City of Sacramento and San Francisco-based firm Perkins + Will, which had initiated master planning for the Sacramento Valley Station, an important regional transportation hub. This project is now registered with the Living Community Challenge.

The Living Future Project Accelerator catalyzed eleven registered Living Building Challenge projects, ranging from a set of townhomes, a demonstration kitchen for Soil Born Farms, and an education center for a local nonprofit.

171

LIVING BUILDING PARTNERS

OWNER
Architectural Nexus

ARCHITECT
Architectural Nexus

LANDSCAPE ARCHITECT
Architectural Nexus

GENERAL CONTRACTOR
MarketOne Builders

MECHANICAL, ELECTRICAL, AND PLUMBING ENGINEERS
Glumac
ACCO Engineered Systems

Royal Electric

STRUCTURAL ENGINEERS
Miyamoto

WATER SYSTEM ENGINEER
2020 ENGINEERING

SOLAR DESIGN/BUILD CONTRACTOR
Hunt Electric

CIVIL ENGINEERS
Warren Consulting Engineers

GEOTECHNICAL ENGINEER
Youngdahl Consulting Group, Inc.

COMMISSIONING AGENT
Capital Engineering Consultants

LIVING WALL DESIGN/BUILD CONTRACTOR
Habitat Horticulture

LOW VOLTAGE SYSTEMS DESIGN/BUILD CONTRACTOR
Valley Communications

PARTNERS AT THE TIME OF LBC CERTIFICATION

SENIOR PRINCIPALS:
Julie Berreth
Jeffery L. Davis
Mark A. Davis
Charles D. Downs
David N. Fletcher
Robb T. Harrop
Kenner Kingston
Scott A. Larkin
Peter Moyes
Douglas A. Thimm
W. Jeffrey Thorpe
Joseph Yee

PRINCIPALS:
David S. Abraham
Holli K. Adams
Aaron L. Arbuckle
Greg E. Brimhall
Victor K. Burbank
Bradford R. Busath
Brian Cassil
Joshua D. Crawford
Jeffrey B. Gardner
Richard Price
Lisa Whoolery Ramidan

PHOTOGRAPHS AND ILLUSTRATIONS

All photos and illustrations by Arch Nexus except as noted:

Chris LaBasco Photography/ Adobe Stock: pg. 11

Lanmas/Alamy Stock Photo: pg. 12

iStock: pg. 13

Information based on Achieving Water Independence In Buildings Report, Central City Concern: pg. 18

Social Economic Environmental Design

Network: pg. 31

Sacramento Historical Society: pg. 35

Flickr Creative Commons: pg. 51

INTERNATIONAL
LIVING FUTURE
INSTITUTE ᔆᴹ

INTERNATIONAL LIVING FUTURE INSTITUTE

The International Living Future Institute (ILFI) is a hub for visionary programs. ILFI offers global strategies for lasting sustainability, partnering with local communities to create grounded and relevant solutions, including green building and infrastructure solutions on scales ranging from single room renovations to neighborhoods or whole cities. ILFI administers the Living Building Challenge, the environment's most rigorous and ambitious performance standard, as well as the Living Product Challenge and Living Community Challenge. In addition, ILFI offers transparency labels through JUST, Declare, and Reveal. Zero Energy and Zero Carbon certification, and Living Future Accreditation are also available. Additionally, ILFI is home to Ecotone Publishing, a unique publishing house dedicated to telling the story of the green building movement's most innovative buildings, thinkers and practitioners.

LIVING BUILDING CHALLENGE

The Living Building Challenge is the built environment's most rigorous performance standard. It calls for the creation of building projects at all scales that operate as cleanly, beautifully, and efficiently as nature's architecture. To be certified under the Challenge, projects must meet a series of ambitious performance requirements, including net zero energy, waste, and water, over a minimum of twelve months of continuous occupancy.

ECOTONE PUBLISHING

Ecotone Publishing is the non-profit publishing arm of ILFI and a key component of ILFI's Communication strategy for sharing expert information about green building technologies and design innovations to create a Living Future. As a publisher, Ecotone produces educational case studies, technical knowledge on renewable energy, plus regenerative and biophilic design, and is the leading source of published information about Living Buildings worldwide. Ecotone also offers professional publishing services to help design firms and organizations document and share their stories, lessons learned, and design solutions with others who are also seeking to address the climate crisis and have a positive impact on their communities.

MORE BOOKS FROM ECOTONE PUBLISHING

Ecotone publications are available online at the Ecotone Bookstore at **living-future.org/bookstore** and at other select retailers.

All proceeds from book sales go to supporting ILFI advocacy and programming.

THE LIVING BUILDING CHALLENGE SERIES

THE LIVING BUILDING CHALLENGE: ROOTS AND RISE OF THE WORLD'S GREENEST STANDARD
by Mary Adam Thomas

BUILDING IN BLOOM
by Mary Adam Thomas

LIVING BUILDING EDUCATION
by Chris Hellstern

GENERATION GREEN
by Michael D. Berrisford

DESERT RAIN HOUSE
by Juliet Grable

THE GREENEST BUILDING
by Mary Adam Thomas

BROCK ENVIRONMENTAL CENTER FOR A LIVING CHESAPEAKE
by Juliet Grable

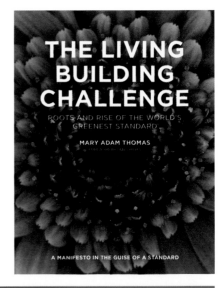

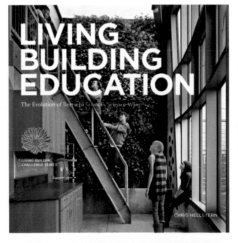

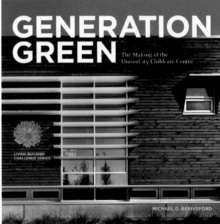

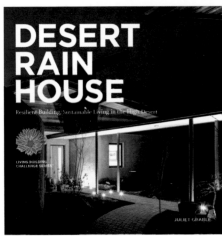

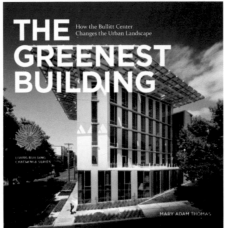

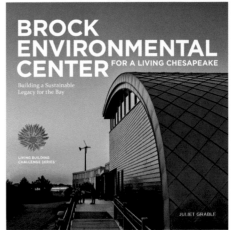

REGENERATIVE RETROFIT: *California's First Living Building*